Scientists Behind the Inventors

SCIENTISTS
Behind the
INVENTORS

By Roger Burlingame

New York

HARCOURT, BRACE & WORLD, INC.

All quotations used in this book are acknowledged in the Bibliography, Section II, at the back of the book. The sources to which key numbers in the text refer are listed numerically in that section.

The author and the publisher acknowledge permission from Doubleday & Company to quote passages from *Madame Curie* by Eve Curie, translated by Vincent Sheean, copyright 1937 by Doubleday & Company, Inc.; and from William Sloane Associates, Inc. to quote from *The Universe and Dr. Einstein* by Lincoln Barnett, copyright 1948 by Harper & Brothers, copyright 1948, 1950, 1957 by Lincoln Barnett.

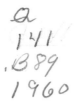

Acknowledgments

In the bibliography at the end of this volume I have listed those books, periodicals, and documents that have provided my sources along with some others that make good collateral reading. But I want especially to acknowledge a few on which I have leaned most heavily. On the general subject of basic scientific research, I have had much inspiration from a little volume by the editors of *Fortune: The Mighty Force of Research.* Two classic biographies, Vallery-Radot's *Life of Pasteur* and Eve Curie's *Madame Curie,* and one autobiography, Michael Pupin's *From Immigrant to Inventor,* have been essential springboards for my study of those scientists. Then there is that remarkable little book by Lincoln Barnett, *The Universe and Doctor Einstein*—the only study of the relativity theories I have ever seen that simplifies without oversimplifying and gives the layman a real glimpse—fragmentary though it must be—into that beautiful world of space that lies beyond all conventional human concepts.

I want to thank the librarians of the New York Public Library and the Engineering Societies Library of New York City for making many primary sources available to me. My old friend William A. W. Krebs, Jr., has come again, as many times before, to my rescue with helpful advice and much valuable material from the files of the Arthur D. Little Company of which he is an officer. Dr. William A. Burns, Coordinator of Popular Publications of The American Museum of Natural History, has given this a careful reading. And I am indebted to Mrs. Russell A. Loring for patient and careful stenographic help.

Contents

Scientists Behind the Inventors

ONE

The Greatest Mystery Story

Discovery and invention are sometimes confused. Essentially, however, they are quite distinct. Discovery is the finding of something that has always been there, though its existence or its meaning has remained hidden. Invention is the design of something new to be made from known materials. America, for example, was discovered; the United States was invented. America had always been there, though its existence was unknown, at least to Europeans, until navigating explorers found it. But the United States was a combination of known materials: land, law, and people.

In the natural sciences, the definitions still hold. Faraday, we say (or Joseph Henry), discovered electromagnetism; the force had always been there but it had not been understood—its meaning had been hidden. After it was understood, it was used in the invention of telegraphs, dynamos, and motors. To Heinrich Hertz is attributed the discovery of radio waves; Marconi and others used the discovery combined with various known devices and materials to invent wireless telegraphy, radiotelephony, television, and radar.

The word "science"—often loosely used by Americans—has, therefore, two forms: basic or fundamental science, once called "pure" science, which is concerned with discovery, and applied science or invention. The two are to a great extent dependent on each other. With our civilization's constantly increasing complexity of instruments, machines, and processes, they are becoming more so. The kind of Yankee ingenuity that produced the cotton gin or the revolver could not have designed the transistor or the coaxial cable or electronic scanning. On the other hand, some of today's great triumphs of invention have led inquiring minds into new realms of discovery: such devices as telescopes and microscopes, computers, photographic instruments, and chemical processes have opened new vistas in astronomy or afforded new vision into the constitution of matter.

A fascinating example of invention leading to discovery was provided by an engineer named Karl Jansky in 1931. Jansky had been assigned the task of finding the cause of static that interfered with transatlantic radiotelephone messages. It was a perfectly practical assignment for a radio engineer. No one supposed the inquiry would need the wide knowledge of a scientist to do such simple trouble-shooting. But the peculiar kind of hissing noise Jansky kept hearing in the phones continued to puzzle him because he could prove that none of the usual causes of static—atmospheric disturbances, interference from other transmitters, or power-line noise—was responsible. Finally, his guesses turned toward the skies, and he found the source of the noise in the center of the Milky Way, a galaxy 26,000 light years away!

Perhaps nothing shows the interplay between "pure" and applied science better than the old story of the so-called Edison Effect. Thomas Edison thought of himself as an inventor, not a scientist. He had no real scientific education of the sort that made Joseph Henry and Willard Gibbs into great men of science. His talent was ingenuity; his success came from the infinite patience that is needed for repeated trial and error with solid materials. He was little concerned with the laws of physics. He admitted his ignorance of mathematics, saying: "I can always hire a mathematician."

Early in the 1880's when he was working to perfect his incandescent lamps, he noticed a discoloration of the inside of the bulbs that showed after much use. Evidently particles of carbon were moving from the hot filament to the glass. An assistant in Edison's laboratory pointed out that the discoloration was uneven and suggested that part of the filament was discharging carbon while another part was not. A series of experiments showed that only the negatively charged end of the filament was shooting the carbon particles, whereas the positive end was not.

To the practical-minded Edison this was a curious phenomenon for which he could see no application. He recorded it in a notebook (as he recorded everything) and forgot it. Actually he was on the threshold of a discovery that has led to a complete transformation of our understanding of physics. If his genius had been that of a scientist rather than that of an inventor, he could have opened the door on that long vista of electronic and radio wave theories that have changed the face of the world.

When the news of the Edison Effect got to England, it began to torment some inquiring minds. It confirmed the observations that had already puzzled John Ambrose Fleming, a young professor of mathematics and physics who was acting, at the time, as consultant to the Edison Light Company of London. Reading of Edison's experiments, he began to ask himself *why* a hot filament should bombard the inside of an incandescent lamp bulb with carbon particles. Edison had simply stated that it did so; having then seen no possible use for the discovery, he had let it go at that. But Fleming, who had a scientific education as well as an ingenious flair, believed that if he could answer the question *why*, he could give the Edison Effect a use.

His colleagues in the London Edison Light Company took the discoloration of the bulbs for granted. "It seemed," he later wrote, "too trifling to notice. But in science it is the trifles that count. The little things of today may develop into the great things of tomorrow." Fleming refused to take anything for granted. Over several years he made experiments with lamps equipped with several kinds of filament. Finally in the course of his investigation of the basic cause of the Edison Effect, he came upon a use for it that had far-reaching results in advancing the practice of electrical communication in the world.

The particles of carbon that shot off the hot filament were evidently negatively electrified. None of them was positive. He proved this by catching these particles on a positively charged metal plate—following the old law that positive attracts negative. It then occurred to him that he had built a valve through which only negative impulses could pass. If this valve were then tied into an alternating current circuit—in which the impulses constantly changed from negative to positive and back again—it would eliminate the positive impulses and so change the alternating current into a direct current. This would be valuable to rectify not only commercial alternating currents produced by dynamos but also the high-frequency wireless currents with which Marconi was working. Marconi then used this Fleming valve as a detector of radio waves, and it thus became the forerunner of all modern radio reception devices.

This was not, however, the end of the Edison Effect once it had got into the hands of the scientists. Fleming had discovered that only negatively charged particles jumped from the hot filament, and a great invention had come out of the discovery. But there was something about the force that carried the particles that was still unexplained. Perhaps Fleming would, in time, have answered that question too. But another English physicist working independently of Fleming found that the vehicles that carried the bits of carbon were "electrons." Sir Joseph John Thomson did not make his discovery through direct study of the Edison Effect. But as soon as he had isolated the electron as a tiny particle that always carried a negative charge of electricity, it was instantly recognized as the jumper in the bulb. The electron, of course, had a far greater meaning than that visible in the Edison Effect, for when it was shown to be an element in the structure of the atom and thus an electrical ingredient of all matter, it revolutionized the whole of physics, and scientists all over the world had to plunge into their research from a new springboard.

Then, finally, the bulb with its bombarding filament crossed the ocean again when the Fleming valve came into the hands of the American inventor, Lee De Forest. De Forest introduced what he called a "grid" between Fleming's filament and his electron-catching plate. He connected the grid with a battery and so added energy to the electrons. This was the first amplifier and was the basis of the three-electrode thermionic vacuum tube, which not only detected and amplified radio waves but also actually generated them. De Forest's so-called "audion" has, as we know, become essential to all radio and television broadcasting. De Forest made his invention in 1906, and it has taken a good many engineers and other applied scientists to build our present great network of communication about it. But however much the devices of today may have been improved and perfected and polished, they may all trace their ancestry back to the curious phenomenon that Edison noted and forgot and that might never have borne fruit unless its mystery had tormented a scientist who knew enough to ask questions.

Meanwhile, Thomson's discovery in the purest realm of pure science has blossomed into almost countless electronic inventions. It would not be accurate to say that the Edison Effect was the father of the discovery of the electron, but we can certainly call it an uncle or a cousin.

The story of the Edison Effect gives only one example of the importance of scientific background to great engineering development. This book will give many others. You will notice that, up to a certain point, Americans—with a few notable exceptions—were far more interested in invention than in discovery; in engineering than in the physical laws it applied; in mechanisms rather than in mathematical mechanics. We dug mines in ignorance of geology, we smelted iron and forged steel with almost no knowledge of chemistry, and we built engines without awareness that there existed a science of thermodynamics.

But all this was natural enough. The men and women who settled this country were daily confronted with overwhelming problems that had to be solved quickly by the nearest available means if the people were to survive at all. Work had to be done with a shortage of labor. Women and children had to do a full share of the work, helping the men even in their defense against Indian attack. Anyone who reads of the terrible covered wagon treks across the plains and through the mountain passes, continually menaced by heat, floods, Indian enemies, and the attacks of wild beasts, or who studies records of the primitive farming methods or the crude making of tools, can see that there was little time for the long quiet thought that basic scientific research demands. As men faced the immense unknowns of the morrow, what chance was there for the long-range view that must always be held by the inquirer into the dark corners of the universe where the causes of our physical phenomena are hid?

In America in the pioneer period, labor-saving machines had to be devised; firearms had to be produced in quantity for defense and for hunting; canals, roads, and then railroads had to be constructed, steamboats and locomotives designed and built, bridges thrown over streams—all these by ingenious use of the nearest means at hand with very little mathematics, physics, or chemistry. The mechanical and engineering feats that were performed with so little schooling seem almost miraculous. It is not surprising that there was waste, for some of which we are paying today: waste of forests, of soil, of game—even of human life.

The time came, however, when needs became too complex to be met by these crude rule-of-thumb solutions. Fortunately for the United States, great things were happening during this pioneer period in the more settled centers of Europe. There, where there was no longer conflict with the savage circumstances of nature in the raw, men had time to contemplate nature's mysteries.

While the first settlers were starving in Virginia, Galileo Galilei in Italy was exploring the heavens with telescopes of his own design and making discoveries that profoundly affected later astronomic research. He had already evolved theories about the pendulum that made it an immense aid to clock invention and construction. While Americans were chopping down forests on the frontiers of Massachusetts, Pennsylvania, and Virginia, Otto von Guericke in Germany was paving the way for the electrical discoveries of the only American scientist worthy of the name in the mid-eighteenth century, Benjamin Franklin. While women and children were being massacred in New England towns, Isaac Newton in England was making discoveries and stating fundamental physical laws that served mankind for two centuries. While Americans were fighting the French and Indians in western New York and Pennsylvania and in the Ohio Valley, Luigi Galvani in Bologna was discovering the galvanic current, and while the patriots of the colonies were fighting for their independence, another Italian, Alessandro Volta, found a chemical source of electric current.

In the nineteenth century, the Frenchman, Ampère; the Germans, Ohm and von Helmholtz; the Dane, Oersted; and the great Englishmen, Faraday, William Thomson, and James Clerk Maxwell, laid bases for the developments that brought the United States to leadership of the world in electrical industry. Until the 1900's most American mining engineers studied the theory of their profession in French and German schools; our chemists were so few that we were unable to start a chemical industry in this country until after World War I; our knowledge of bacteriology came from France; and our great recent achievements in horticulture and animal husbandry stem mainly from discoveries made or theories evolved by European biologists, botanists, or zoologists.

In all this time there was a mere handful of native American scientists who reached European standards. They were great men to be sure. Franklin's scientific achievements were more celebrated abroad than in his own country. Joseph Henry and Willard Gibbs made contributions that were recognized in every part of the civilized world. Benjamin Silliman of Yale, besides being a distinguished geologist, established in his *American Journal of Science and the Arts* one of the great scientific periodicals of all time. But when he did this, there was only one other scientific paper in the United States, whereas Germany had fifty and in England, France, and Italy there were thirty-five! Later, Samuel Langley and Percival Lowell made important researches in astronomy. But some men that we claim as top-flight American scientists, such as the naturalist Jean Louis Agassiz, the mathematician Charles Steinmetz, and the physicist Michael Pupin, were born and educated abroad.

Meanwhile, as transportation, communication, and manufacture became the dominant American necessities, there were prodigies of invention and engineering that made the United States the industrial giant that by the twentieth century she had become. The vast railroad network and in its wake the huge quantity production of steel, the design and building of the automatic machine tools and electric motors that brought mass production, the development of electric lighting and the long-distance transmission of electric power, the magnetic telegraph, the telephone, and, soon after the turn of the century, the airplane and the low-cost motor car—these things punctuated the nation's growth. That the theoretical basis of a practical invention came to this new, raw wilderness from overseas was inevitable: we borrowed science from abroad just as we took religion, literature, and the arts, and, indeed, the people themselves.

Then, after World War I, a change began. The war dealt a terrible blow to the scientific research that for more than two centuries had been going on in the cloistered security of European laboratories. It also brought new incentives to America. For example, the immense German chemical industry that had led the world broke wide open, and many of the precious German patents passed to the United States as part of war reparations. For the first time, we were able to establish a chemical industry of our own. The almost incredibly rapid progress thus made between the wars gave momentum to chemical research in the universities and the foundation laboratories.

As World War II approached, forced migration to America gave us some of the world's greatest men of science. Fugitive from Hitler's brutal racial purges came many of the charter members of Princeton's Institute for

Advanced Study, including that greatest of all mathematicians and physicists—perhaps the greatest scientist in history—Albert Einstein. Edward Teller, an exile from Hungarian anti-Semitism, is today called "the father of the H bomb." Finally when, during World War II, Americans took the ball of nuclear research from such distinguished foreign scientists as Niels Bohr and Enrico Fermi and carried it to devastating effect over Japan, it was evident that American basic research had at last come into its own. From now on it was certain that whatever "Edison Effects" might occur would never again be filed away in notebooks and forgotten.

The change is pointed up by the record of Nobel prizes awarded to Americans for outstanding work in physics, chemistry, medicine, and physiology. From 1901 through 1939, only 15 out of 128 of these prizes were won by American scientists. But from 1943 through 1956 Americans were given 34 out of 67—more than half of all the awards made. This dates the beginning of the new look of American science pretty accurately: the change came while Europe, between 1939 and 1943, was fighting the most terrible war in history—a war that never directly touched our continent. There was, therefore, much tragedy connected with our progress. The war's end left wrecked and weary Europe behind us in many ways. This led Columbia's Nobel-Prize-winning professor, Isidor Isaac Rabi, to remark in 1954: "When I first went to Europe a quarter century ago, *I* was provincial; when I went to Europe after the war, it was Europe that had become provincial."

Unfortunately, the majority of the American people did not appreciate the change that had so forcibly struck Professor Rabi. Perhaps too many of us were still thinking of the old American tradition that our job was to make useful things and things that would sell, instead of inquiring into the whys and hows of the universe. Many of our industrial establishments were obsessed with the idea of making more and better gadgets. Enormous quantities of quite useless articles flooded our market; our automobile makers spent fortunes on research to find unnecessary luxuries for our cars or to satisfy the pride of people who were trying to "keep up with the Joneses." So a great deal of money was spent for what is called "committed" research—that is, study of new products or processes or engineering projects or the improvement of old ones. At the same time, the brilliant basic scientists of the postwar era were struggling toward their discoveries with too little support—too little money and too little moral backing.

Unhappily there developed, in these postwar years, a strange attitude toward intellectuals—thinkers of all kinds. Even the scientists who were really working for the future welfare of mankind were looked upon as long-haired screwballs. What were they doing shut away in their laboratories, their "ivory towers," fussing over mathematical symbols that no one could understand? It became fashionable to talk with contempt about "egg-heads." Thus many students reluctantly turned away from scientific pursuits or from social sciences such as philosophy or psychology lest they be laughed at by their fellows. Others, tempted by basic research, were afraid there was too little money in it. There was, you see, a vicious circle: the reason there was too little money was that there was too little public interest. The "egghead scorners"—many of them rich men able to endow university activities—were keeping the money away from basic research or giving it instead to business education.

During these years some people thought it unwise to appear too curious about what went on behind the Iron Curtain. People who knew "too much" about Russia were branded communists or fellow travelers. This was the most unreasonable fad of all. If a country is a potential enemy, the more you know about it, the better able you will be to fight if it becomes a real enemy. Finally, it was too often assumed that all Russians were dumb, illiterate, dirty, uneducated, lying, and cynical people, and that neither science nor engineering could possibly develop in so backward a country, dominated by a tyrannical government.

All of these attitudes combined to damage our new-born American scientific prestige, but they also blinded too many of us to the extraordinary advances that our cold-war enemy was making. Our scientists, to be sure, knew better and were less surprised than the rest of us when it was found that Russia had the A-bomb and then the H-bomb. Yet many Americans supposed she must have got the "know how" of those things from us. Then, suddenly, one day Russia shot into the sky something that we did not have.

The unexpected revelation in the first week of October, 1957, was truly stunning. Overnight the faddist thinking was reversed. There, in despised Russia, it was the eggheads who had triumphed; the long-haired scientists working silently in their ivory towers had made it possible for the engineers to put a satellite into an orbit hundreds of miles above the earth!

Actually, we blamed ourselves too much. After three and a half years of war no one thinks quite straight. Various propaganda had put us through a lot of mental acrobatics. After hating Russia for years, we suddenly, in 1941, had to turn around and love her because she was on our side. Then after the violent hatred we had felt toward the Japanese and the Germans, we were obliged after the war was over to embrace them as allies against the old villain Russia who had returned to her evil ways. We were then carried away by the greatest prosperity we had ever known, and we became sure that anyone who hinted that we might be too rich was a communist conspirator who must be put in jail before he bombed Wall Street. With all this confusion and bewilderment, it was no wonder that we were stunned by the terrifying reality that suddenly beeped at us from the skies.

We have, of course, settled back somewhat after the

shock and we have become more realistic. We have studiously examined the background of Russia's sensational success. We have seen that to attain such levels in a country that was, a generation ago, 75 per cent illiterate must have required an educational system on which enormous energies were concentrated. Investigation of this system shows a steady program of incentives, rewards, and prestige to the very persons we have called long-haired or eggheads. In Russia we find the graduates of schools and universities honored by the government and respected by the people. We find money poured out for educational purposes, teachers given excellent living facilities and well-equipped school or university buildings, large libraries, and laboratories described by those who have seen them as nothing short of superb.

Having had this startling look behind the Iron Curtain, we have taken stock of our own education. We have seen many things that have to be corrected. We are now finding some ways, for instance, for the brilliant boys and girls to go ahead faster toward professional work than their slower contemporaries. We must come nearer the European (not necessarily the Russian) program of getting our boys and girls ready for their careers sooner. This may cut out some of our beloved extracurricular activities, but the country's need for scientists and engineers in this critical time is too pressing to wait.

Obviously our young people cannot be forced into careers as they may be in a totalitarian state. American youth is not subject to such regimentation. Nor should

young Americans, in their zeal to see their country sur-
pass Russia in scientific triumphs, force themselves into
careers for which they are not suited. But they should
carefully examine those professions that will be much
in demand in the future to make sure that there is not
something so fascinating in them that they will want to
dedicate their lives to them.

At the top of the list of such professions stands that
of basic scientific research. A government official of the
pre-Sputnik era remarked scornfully that "basic research is when you don't know what you're doing." He
meant that as it was not directed toward a known goal, no
"hardware" was likely to come out of it very quickly. He
little realized that, actually, he was defining adventure.
As Dr. Alan Waterman, Director of the National Science
Foundation, has said of the basic research specialist:
"The unexpected is what he thrives on." The "appeal of
basic research," he says, is "the appeal of exploring the
unknown whatever it may reveal. . . ." To Dr. Vannevar Bush, who has led some of the most important in-
vestigations of the atomic age, the function of basic research is a peculiarly American one—the opening of new
frontiers. The United States, he says, "opened the seas
to clipper ships and furnished land to pioneers. Although
these frontiers have more or less disappeared, the frontier
of science remains."

Obviously, basic research in the natural or physical sciences cannot be wholly undirected. But it is directed by
and toward ideas rather than by and toward things. An

investigator into the laws of motion does not see an automobile or a streamlined train at the end of his road. But usually a scientific researcher has something by which to systematize his work—often a belief, or what he calls a hypothesis. For example, Galileo was convinced that two objects of different weights dropped from the same height would hit the ground at the same instant, and he spent much time (and got into serious trouble with the anti-eggheads) proving his belief and working out a law stating why the phenomenon was true. Einstein, believing that the velocity of light was constant regardless of the motion of its source or its observer, proved his hypothesis and worked out mathematical equations to express it that have altered the scientific concepts of the universe. It is from such beliefs and suppositions that a basic researcher may take off, though where his exploration will lead him he cannot tell. Sometimes it will lead him to scrap his hypothesis entirely and start fresh from another.

Scientists everywhere testify to the excitement of this carrying of light into darkness. To most of them the sense of adventure is worth far more than the money they might make in business or industry. In an article that appeared in *Fortune* in June, 1954, entitled "The Young Scientists," by Francis Bello, this feeling is well expressed.

When scientists talk about their work, the word "fun" is never long absent. "People don't understand," says one of the brightest young physicists, "that scientists are just a bunch of guys trying to have the most fun they know how. If I knew anything more fun, I'd be doing it." [1]

And in the same article:

> "I don't know how other people get thrills in life," says one outstanding physicist, "but to me the biggest thrill is in seeing a new effect for the first time. It may happen only once or twice a year but it's worth all the drudgery that precedes it. It's like shoveling dirt in a gold field and suddenly turning up a nugget. When this happens, it spoils you and you'll never settle for less." [2]

Bello's article is included in a volume called *The Mighty Force of Research*. This book tells the stories of some of the important discoveries of history. Consistent with the idea of the title, these accounts are of research on which later inventions have been based, although no invention may have been in the mind of the scientist. He was making his inquiry for its own sake, to increase the world's fund of knowledge. Unlike the inventor, he had no motive to keep his discoveries secret. His reward came not in a monopoly of his design but in answering some of the millions of questions that curious minds have asked since the beginnings of human consciousness.

Behind the Steam Engine

Young James Watt stood in his workshop staring in bewilderment at the model of the Newcomen engine he had been ordered to repair. The repairs had been easy; but when they were finished, he could not resist experimenting with the little model. The atmospheric engine that Newcomen had invented some fifty years before had been at work in flooded coal mines ever since, and the complaints of the mine owners had grown louder year by year. Its job was to pump the water out of the deeper mines so that the miners could get at the coal beneath it. But the complaint was that it used more coal than it helped to mine.

Watt's understanding of machinery was almost instinctive. From a glance at any piece of mechanism, he could tell precisely how it worked. If its functioning was faulty, he could discover what was wrong with so rapid a reasoning that his friends thought him intuitive. His fingers seemed to feel out the trouble; then he could either repair the defect or improve on the machine by inventing new devices or making new parts. It was this apparent genius that had persuaded the authorities of the University of Glasgow to hire him as its curator of precision instruments and to give him a workshop in which he could repair or remake or even invent these delicate mechanisms. The telescopes, quadrants, balances, and other instruments that kept him busy were primitive enough compared with such things today, but in the mid-eighteenth century they were the best of their kinds. Watt's handling of them fascinated the professors, and his willingness to talk and explain greatly endeared him to them, so that he was seldom alone in his room.

But this time he was really puzzled. There was nothing especially complicated about the Newcomen atmospheric engine. It was really not a "steam" engine at all; the steam was used merely to create a vacuum so that air pressure could go to work. There was a cylinder and a piston. Steam was shot into the cylinder below the piston. Then cold water was shot into the steam to condense it. When the steam had been turned into water, a vacuum was left and the pressure of the atmosphere above the piston forced the piston into it. Then a weighted beam pulled the piston back, and the whole operation was repeated.

What puzzled Watt was the immense amount of water that had to be injected into the steam to cool and liquefy it. When the water was first shot into the cylinder, instead of liquefying the steam, it turned into steam itself. Somehow there was much more heat in the steam than the thermometer showed. When Watt put a thermometer in the steam, it only registered approximately 212° Fahrenheit—the proper boiling point of water. But why was this extra heat concealed and where did it go? Tormented, as always, by mystery, James Watt determined to find out.

He attached a tube to the spout of a teakettle. He put the other end of the tube into a glass vessel containing water at room temperature. He then put a measured quantity of water in the kettle and heated it until steam came from the spout into the tube and so into the glass vessel. He expected the steam to be condensed as it entered the cool water. To his amazement the steam made the water boil. Furthermore, calculations showed that the water in the kettle, when it had been converted into steam, had heated six times its own weight of cool water to the boiling point! Thus he had proved what he had wanted to prove, but there was still no apparent reason for it. Throughout the experiment, the thermometer had never risen above 212°.

Fortunately, James Watt had a friend among the university's professors to whom he could take his problems. Doctor Joseph Black, who occupied the chair of anatomy and chemistry, was intensely interested in everything James Watt did because, though Black was a "pure" scientist, he believed that every important scientific discovery should, if possible, be used to benefit mankind. This belief was not common in those days when scientists liked to shut themselves up in an ivory tower and avoided "contamination" by the "vulgarities" of industry and business. Yet in Scotland—as opposed to England—there was beginning to be a break in this snobbish tradition, and the universities of Glasgow and Edinburgh led the revolutionary trend.

Day after day, into Watt's little workroom whose two windows looked out on the inner quadrangle of the college, trooped the professors and the teachers who were drawn by the magnet of "Jamie's" personality. There was Robert Dick, professor of "natural philosophy"—the name by which science was then called—who had got Jamie his job at the university; there was John Anderson, who had given Watt the Newcomen engine to repair and so started him on his great career of invention; there was Adam Smith, whose extraordinary book, *Inquiry into the Nature and Causes of the Wealth of Nations,* later brought revolution to the world of economics, and there was the calm, immaculate, perfectly dressed, and poised Doctor Black, who usually entered playing soft melodies on a flute. All of these men were M.D.'s: to become a scientist in Scotland in those days, you had to have a degree as doctor of medicine first.

Finally, trailing these professors, came the tall seventeen-year-old boy John Robison who, even at that age, was about to graduate from the university. Handsome, impulsive, rushing impetuously into everything that interested him, he used to bombard Watt with questions, all of which the inventor answered to the delight of his professional audience. Robison had a boyish habit of hero-worship. Black was the first of his heroes—his flute

playing, he afterward wrote, "thrilled me to the heart"
—but soon he had the same feelings toward Jamie Watt,
and eventually these three, regardless of age differences,
formed an attachment and a companionship that was
never broken, however far they were physically separated.
In point of fact, Robison, one of the most romantic figures in late scientific history, moved far in the British
Navy when, as midshipman at twenty, he took part in the
capture of Quebec from the French and was in the ship
that brought home the body of General Wolfe, killed in
the battle. After this adventure, the young man returned
to become one of the great mathematical teachers of the
period.

Glasgow University—the "college" as its students
called it—was quite different from the institutions of
higher education we know today. The students for the
most part were only fourteen or fifteen years old. They
must have been exceedingly precocious boys, judging by
the advanced subjects they studied. The professors seem
to have had calm and quiet temperaments—wasting no
words—and emotions that were rarely ruffled, taking life
as it came to them. Occasionally there would be a ban-
quet at which the faculty was host to distinguished
guests. At these the men would sit late at their wine, and
probably those who did not fall asleep carried on eru-
dite conversations. Sir William Ramsay, in his life of
Doctor Black, repeats a tale that is characteristic of the
easy-going Scots of the period.

The story is told [Ramsay writes] that during one of the official feasts . . . one of the guests was struck with the pale face of his neighbor, who appeared to be asleep. . . . "What ails Drumshough?" he asked the man beside him: "He's looking gey gash." " 'Sh man," said he, "he's been wi' his Maker thae twa hours." [3]

In this setting, Joseph Black was exceptional. There was an elegance about him, a balance, and an extraordinary peace of mind that set him apart. When he lectured, he talked always in a low voice but with such carrying power that he could be heard in every corner of the largest classroom. But what struck his students most was the neatness with which he performed the chemical experiments that accompanied his lectures. Nothing ever went wrong; he had foreseen every possible emergency.

I have seen him [wrote a student] pour boiling water or boiling acid from a vessel that had no spout into a tube, holding it at such a distance as made the stream's diameter small, and so vertical that not a drop was spilt. While he poured he would mention this adaptation of the height to the diameter as a necessary condition of success. . . . The long table on which the different processes were carried on was as clean at the end of the lecture as it had been before the apparatus was planted upon it. Not a drop of liquid, not a grain of dust remained. [4]

Another student remembered the instant attention Black's presence commanded. "The wildest boy," he wrote, "respected Black. No lad could be irreverent toward a man so pale, so gentle, so elegant and so illustrious."

Black's achievements as a scientist were revolutionary. He has been called the "father of modern chemistry." Having practiced as a physician, he was drawn into chemical experiments by studying various "cures" used in his day for treatment of the kidney stone. Some of these nostrums seem to us to belong in the book of magic rather than in that of medicine—involving powdered snails and eggshells—but much medical practice in those years was in a stage of transition from the ways of the witch doctor, and we often wonder how the patients survived. But, fantastic as it was, it led Doctor Black into studies of limewater and applications of heat and acids to calcic substances, and through these he came to an early awareness of the existence of gases. Up to that time all gases were thought to be air in varying degrees of purity. What we recognize today as oxygen, hydrogen, and so on were called, in Black's day, "impure air." Black showed that what emerged from chalk and lime when heated was not air but something quite different from air. It was, indeed, carbon dioxide, the gas we exhale after air has passed through the lungs. He did not call it "gas" because he doubted that anyone would know what he meant. So he called it "fixed air"—but he knew better, as his notes show.

He made another step forward in measuring carefully all the materials of his experiments. By weighing what went into his reactions and what came out of them, he laid the early foundations of modern chemistry in which weight plays so important a part. Starting on the level he established, the great pioneers, Lavoisier, Priestley, and others, developed the beautiful pattern that, with its laws of combination by weight and by volume, made nineteenth and twentieth century chemical industry possible.

While much of Black's study came later when he had moved from the University of Glasgow to that of Edinburgh, he had already carried out and lectured on his experiments with water in its three stages—ice, liquid, and steam—and on his proof of the heat function in the transition, so he had become the ideal person for Watt to talk to. Indeed, he was, no doubt, the only person in the world who could give a satisfactory answer to the questions conjured up by Watt's teakettle.

Though Watt's main achievement was invention, he had, unlike many other inventors, a scientific mind. He was, indeed, half a scientist. He was never satisfied simply to observe and record a phenomenon as Edison often was. He had to know *why* before he could go on to the next step. Perhaps, because of this, he was congenial with the professors—he could always go halfway to meet them.

We may imagine him interrupting the doctor's flute playing the next time Black came to the workshop, pointing to the model engine and, perhaps, his teakettle, and telling his strange story. Joseph Black smiled.

"Why, Jamie," he said in effect, "haven't you heard of

my theory about latent heat? I've been lecturing on it for two years or so."

"No, I haven't heard about it. I've been too busy here. But now I can't go on until I get the answer to this puzzle."

So Black explained what he thought was the reason for the great amount of heat Watt had found not showing in the thermometer. Black's thinking about this came close to some chemical truths that we understand today, though he could not express it in the terms he used. Water, he believed, whether in the solid, liquid, or vaporized state, was composed of minute particles. (We call them molecules.) In ice the particles were close together; in water, farther apart; in steam, widely separated from one another. To bring about the separation, heat was necessary, but the heat was consumed in doing the job and so it did not show. Where did it go? Why, it became part of the particles themselves and thus could not communicate itself to the thermometer—not at least until the steam was condensed, when it would be released and emerge into the cooler condensing water.

As Black recorded his experiments in his notebook,

when a fluid body is raised to its boiling temperature, by the . . . application of heat, its particles attract to themselves a great quantity of heat and, by this combination, their mutual relation is so changed that they no longer attract each other, gathering into drops and forming a liquid, but avoid each other, separating to at least ten times their former distance . . .[5]

To us, there is something quaint about these particles "absorbing" so much heat that they run away from each other, and, indeed, according to modern belief, Black's theory was erroneous. Our explanation today is that heat is converted into energy and thus becomes "latent." Yet Black's explanation was far above the level of thought in the 1750's and it was a step in the true direction. We must remember, after all, that oxygen had not yet been discovered, that the fact that water was a compound of gases was undreamed of, and heat was believed to be not a force but a substance called "phlogiston," which could be mixed with or separated from other substances! But most important to the progress of civilization, Black's theory cleared up a mystery for Watt, set his mind at rest about the behavior of steam in the Newcomen engine, and left him free to go on to his great invention. As Black had talked, Watt had felt a great elation, knowing that, as he afterward wrote, he had accidentally "stumbled upon one of the material facts by which that beautiful theory is supported."

He now looked again at the Newcomen model. He saw again but with new eyes that the jet of water that condensed the steam in the cylinder also cooled the cylinder so that when new steam was shot into the cylinder, the coolness of the metal tended to condense it and it took a long time to get the cylinder hot enough again to keep the steam intact *as steam*. This was just what Black had told him: in the presence of a cold object the particles of steam could not keep their tendency to avoid each other and so formed into drops of water. Thus much steam was wasted and the whole process was extremely slow.

Watt spent many sleepless nights searching for the remedy for this obvious defect. But as often happens, the harder he worked over it, the more remote the solution seemed to become. Apparently the answer came to him at a moment when his mind was at rest after a long Sunday morning. Perhaps he had slept late in the quiet of the Scotch Sabbath. Perhaps physical exercise freshened his thinking. At any rate, thanks to Watt's habit of constant note-making, we have his simple record of what we should call his "brainstorm."

> It was *in the Green of Glasgow*. I had gone to take a walk on a fine Sabbath afternoon. . . . I was thinking upon the engine at the time and had gone as far as the Herd's house when *the idea came into my mind, that as steam was an elastic body it would rush into a vacuum, and if a communication was made between the cylinder and an exhausted vessel, it would rush into it and might be there condensed without cooling the cylinder. . . . I had not walked further than the golf-house when the whole thing was arranged in my mind.*[6]

At this point the strict Glasgow Sabbath stopped him. Itching to make the experiment, he had to wait till the next morning. The building of the necessary apparatus would have made so much noise that he would surely have been arrested! But perhaps the pause was good for him. Perhaps in the interval, irritated as he may have been, his subconscious mind completed the plan.

But as he went to work on the days following, we know that there was no longer any doubt in his mind. His impetuous friend Robison, whose curiosity about Watt's doings was irrepressible, tells how he burst into Watt's room and discovered Watt sitting with a "little tin cistern" on his lap. When Robison began to quiz him, Watt stopped him. "You need not fash yourself about that, man; I have now made an engine that shall not waste a particle of steam."

Watt's next step was to turn the atmospheric engine into a steam engine. Once he had solved the problem of keeping the cylinder hot, he found that the expansive power of the hot steam could be used on both sides of the piston alternately so that the air pressure was dispensed with and his engine had most of the characteristics of the great prime movers that worked such wonders in the nineteenth and early twentieth centuries.

The rest of James Watt's story of his partnership with Matthew Boulton and the success of the Watt and Boulton works in Soho in England is so familiar that it need not be repeated here. There is one thing, however, that must be emphasized because it has a bearing on the scientific influences on this inventor's thinking. This was Watt's use of Black's discoveries in the realm of thermal equilibrium, which made it possible to estimate in advance precisely how much work each engine could do per unit of fuel. This ratio was what the customers had to know before they bought. They had been discouraged by long, sad experience with the Newcomen pump. But now the performance of a Watt and Boulton engine could be guaranteed in advance and the buyer could know exactly what it would cost him to run his engine. And Watt worked out a precise unit of power that has been used ever since.

He did not originate the term "horsepower," for the work of other prime movers had been compared to what a certain number of horses could do. But this was either guesswork or determination by tests in the individual cases. Watt evolved a universal formula. "Each horse," he stated, "will raise 33,000 pounds one foot high per minute." Thus, for the first time, *horsepower* became an exact, standard unit of measurement.

We see here the insistence on *measurement,* the factor that Black introduced into all his experiments. It is hard to believe that there was a time when this all-important practice in modern science was largely neglected. In almost every sort of work the "rule of thumb" was the gauge. The resulting experiments were haphazard, often pure guesswork. We find exceptional men like Isaac Newton and Benjamin Franklin who were ahead of their time in this respect, but they were not common.

With the association between Black and Watt and between Watt and Dick, Anderson, Robison, and the other professors, we see an early meeting between science and industry and, as it turned out, between science and business. Black, for example, was so interested in Watt's commercial success that he helped finance Watt's early work.

In later years we find Watt a member of the famous Lunar Society (known to the irreverent as "The Lunatics") in which such captains of industry as Josiah Wedgwood, the pottery manufacturer, would spend long, warm evenings in an atmosphere of wine and candlelight talking to such pioneers in pure science as Priestley, the discoverer of oxygen. It was, of course, this marriage, so to speak, between science and industry that brought the world we know into being.

It is true that the reciprocating steam engine has largely disappeared from the American scene, and, indeed, even the steam turbine, except in giant power stations, has given way to internal combustion motors. Nevertheless, the invention of Watt was largely responsible for the Industrial Revolution and the whole complex of machine production—including mass production—that it brought in its train.

The brief story of Joseph Black's death in 1799 gives us as vivid a picture of this great man of science as any that has been drawn.

> Being at table . . . and having his cup in his hand when the last stroke of the pulse was to be given, he appeared to have set it down on his knees, which were joined together, and in the action expired without spilling a drop, as if an experiment had been purposely made to evince the facility with which he departed.[7]

THREE

Evangelist of Science

In a hot room, heavy with a stifling acrid odor, a preoccupied man stood over a stove and watched the simmering pot from which the stench came. In the excitement that always possessed him during his experiments, he had forgotten his poverty, the debts for which from time to time he had been thrown into prison, and the illness of his wife and son. He had forgotten, too, the severe advice of his well-meaning friends who had been in the room most of the day, begging him to give up this work for what they called a lost cause and to go back to the hardware business in which he had started. Now they had gone, and Charles Goodyear was alone with the hot stove and the stinking pot on its top.

Suddenly he felt a hand on his shoulder and he turned. The tension in his face relaxed. An old friend had come so softly into the room that Goodyear had not heard him. He knew as he looked into the serene eyes that this friend would not scold or harass him.

"So, Professor Silliman," he said. "They tell me it's hopeless."

"I know better. I've watched you, Charles Goodyear, for a long time."

When Benjamin Silliman made a statement, it was almost impossible not to believe him. His quiet confidence was quickly contagious. His magnetism not only held his classes of eager boys at Yale College, but, lately, it had reached out to spellbind men and women in the lecture halls of New Haven and Boston and New York. The name of Silliman drew such crowds that the largest auditorium would not hold them all and the lectures had to be repeated for the overflow. And it was the name of Silliman rather than that word "chemistry," still mysterious, still magic in America in those first decades of the nineteenth century, that drew them. This man could make them understand, even the most ignorant of them; and if they did not entirely understand his words, his dramatic chemical demonstrations made everything clear.

Goodyear had turned back to the stove when Silliman spoke again.

"There's a new smell today, Goodyear."

"Sulphur."

"You're on the right track. Let me know as soon as success comes. I will make a noise about it. I will tell them in my classes at Yale College, and I will use my influence to make it known."

Goodyear's celebrated "accident" followed Silliman's visit. Inventors and scientists do not altogether believe in accidents. "In the field of experimentation," said Pasteur, "chance favors only the prepared mind." Thus, when Goodyear accidentally spilled the mixture out of his pot on the hot stove, it was not accidental that he recognized the result as the vulcanized rubber he sought. Nor was it accidental that he had spent countless hours of trial and error working toward this result. His mind was truly "prepared."

When he was sure, Goodyear told Silliman. The professor came, verified the result, and signed a paper testifying to the invention. Many years later, when Benjamin Silliman was delivering a course of lectures in Washington, Goodyear saw him again. He had come with his wife and son to listen.

"If it had not been for you, sir," Goodyear told him, "I should long since have been in my grave; all my relations and friends have discouraged me and you alone sustained me by your opinion and your influence."

It was characteristic of Silliman to encourage Goodyear. He spent much of his life helping inventors with scientific information and with advice based on his own deep study. Yet in the sense that we use the word today, he was not precisely a scientist, for he did little original research and made few new discoveries. Rather, he was an evangelist of science, preaching the gospels of chemistry, physics, and geology. As such, he was exactly what this new American nation needed most in the first half of the nineteenth century. When he began, his was almost a lone voice in a wilderness of ignorance. By the time of his death during the Civil War, he had brought science alive not only to the young men he inspired to careers of theoretical teaching and research but also to practical men as well—inventors who could turn the information to profit. And, perhaps most important of all, he had established a medium of communication through which scientists the world over could exchange views and promote their common interests.

We have come to know that scientific knowledge must pass through three stages before it can reach its full effectiveness. First, there is discovery made by the experimental researcher and his statement of the laws based upon it. Second, there is the publication of that discovery and the teaching that diffuses or spreads the information. Finally, there is the application of the discovery to some useful or practical purpose. Silliman was the middleman in this sequence. He did for America what the great scientific societies of Europe with their papers and the records of their "transactions" do for their countries, and he did it almost singlehanded.

Like other scientists whom we shall meet, young Ben Silliman, when he graduated from Yale College, had not planned for himself a scientific career. In the 1790's boys rarely thought of such a thing. The respectable vocation for a young man of Ben's social standing was in the ministry or the law. The emphasis in Yale College was on theology. It had been founded under the auspices of the Calvinist churches of the New Haven Colony; its early presidents or rectors were Congregational ministers; and, in contrast to "godless" Harvard, it enforced strict orthodoxy. Also, although "the arts and sciences" had been specified in Yale's charter, their teaching was permitted only if it passed certain theological tests. So, in most of its first century, the kind of science that gained such headway in the great universities of Europe never entered Yale's curriculum and, indeed, was regarded with suspicion by her faculty and trustees.

During the Revolutionary War, however, the election of Ezra Stiles as president brought in a change. Stiles was deeply interested in almost every branch of "natural philosophy," as science was called, from botany to astronomy, and he inspired curiosity about these things in the students. It was during his administration that Eli Whitney studied, and under his influence Whitney's ingenuity in the construction and use of scientific instruments developed. Thus, by 1792, when Whitney graduated, Yale College had become aware of the physical laws, and Benjamin Silliman, entering in that same year, soon felt the change.

To every student of Yale's history, these two, Silliman and Whitney, must always be associated. Graduating within four years of each other, they became pioneers in the American fields of pure and applied science. In 1792, to be sure, these men who—in their separate ways as teacher and inventor—influenced the course of the nation's history were far apart in age and condition. Whitney, the son of a farmer, handicapped by poverty and illness, was long delayed in his education and was a mature man of twenty-seven when he finished Yale. Silliman, born into an old Connecticut family of means and distinction, his schooling unimpaired by ill-health, was able to enter college at the tender age of thirteen.

. . .

According to the superstitions current at the time of his birth, Benjamin Silliman should have been frail in mind and body—if not, indeed, a monster or an imbecile, for three months before he was born his mother suffered a severe shock of the sort that was believed to have a devastating effect on the promised child.

The year was 1779. The Revolution was in full swing. The British, already in possession of New York and Long Island, were concentrating their attack upon the hard core of resistance in Connecticut. One of the principal instigators and supporters of this resistance was Brigadier General Gold Selleck Silliman, who had distinguished himself in the siege of Danbury and the battle of Ridgefield. His home was at Fairfield, across the sound from the enemy stronghold in Long Island. If they could take this officer prisoner, the British believed, the resistance would melt away. Accordingly, in the words of his son's autobiography:

A secret boat expedition was sent by Sir Henry Clinton from New York—manned chiefly by Tories. . . . They entered Black Rock Harbor at Fairfield, drew their boat into the sedge, and leaving one of their number as a guard, the remaining eight proceeded . . . to my father's house, which at the midnight hour was all quiet and the family asleep. On May 1st, 1779, between twelve and one o'clock A.M., the house was violently assaulted by large heavy stones, banging against both doors, with oaths, imprecations and threats. My father, being awaked from a sound sleep, seized two loaded guns standing at his bedside, rushed to the front windows, and by the light of the moon seeing armed men in the stoop or portico, he thrust the muzzle of a musket through a pane of glass and pulled the trigger but there was only a flash in the pan, and the gun did not go off. Percussion caps were then unknown and muskets were fired by flint and steel. Instantly the windows were dashed in, and the ruffians were upon him. . . . These rude men, bearing guns with fixed bayonets, followed my father into the bedroom—a terrific sight to his wife, she being in bed, with her little son Gold Selleck, not eighteen months old, lying upon her arm . . .[8]

The general was taken by his captors to Long Island, and it was more than a year later that he was first able to see his new son, Benjamin, born just fourteen weeks after the capture.

As he grew up, the boy had the appearance of seriousness, which earned him the epithet of Sober Ben, but from some of his youthful diaries and letters it is reasonable to suspect that there were lapses in his devotion to studious pursuits. He was exceedingly handsome; it is probable that he was not only aware of his good looks but aware also that the girls turned to look at him. At what age his delight in the other sex began is not clear, but it is certain that, in his freshman year, it often diverted him from his homework. In the sporadic journal in which he confessed his boyish vanities and ambitions, we find a number of occasions on which he threw down his books and spent the evening dancing.

He was next to the youngest in his class. That there

should have been a freshman younger than thirteen in Yale College suggests that American boys were more mature then than now. But Yale was also much less mature than in these middle years of the twentieth century. There was, besides the president, only one professor. The other teachers were called tutors. The total undergraduate enrollment was under two hundred. These youths made what Ezra Stiles called a "bundle of wild fire." The restless spirit of the Revolution in which many of their fathers had participated moved among them. Discipline was so difficult to enforce that, according to Stiles, "the Diadem of a President is a Crown of Thorns." One of the rules he insisted upon, in order to ensure respect for their betters, was that "undergraduates are to be uncovered, and are forbidden to wear their hats (unless in stormy weather) in the front dooryard of the President's or Professor's house or within ten rods of the person of the President, eight rods of the Professor, and five rods of a tutor." This rule (which would be quite meaningless in this hatless day) did not, however, protect the tutors, who dared not go out alone at night for fear of a beating by the students.

Altogether, it seems hardly a congenial atmosphere for a quiet lad like "Sober Ben"; yet he thrived upon it and no graduate of Yale has ever felt a deeper loyalty to his alma mater. His undergraduate diary reflects a normal boy's enjoyment of life along with some solemn self-criticism and rules of conduct that remind one of the introspection of young Ben Franklin. Years later, he wrote nostalgically of his first exposure, in college, to the light of science. In the Yale he knew in the 1790's

> . . . a single room was appropriated to apparatus in physics. . . . It was papered on the walls; the floor was sanded, and the window-shutters were always kept closed except when visitors or students were introduced. There was an air of mystery about the room, and we entered it with awe, increasing to admiration after we had seen something of the apparatus and the experiments. There was an air-pump, an electrical machine of the cylinder form, a whirling table, a telescope of medium size, and some of smaller dimensions, a quadrant, a set of models for illustrating the mechanical powers, a condensing fountain . . . a theodolite, and a magic lantern—the wonder of Freshmen.[9]

Yale's own professor, Josiah Meigs, seems to have known much of what was then known of "natural philosophy." He had read of Doctor Black's discovery of latent heat and of Lavoisier's further researches in thermodynamics, which he presented as chemistry; and the boy Ben was as excited about it as James Watt had been.

> Professor Josiah Meigs [remembered the mature Silliman] . . . delivered lectures on natural philosophy from the pulpit of the College Chapel. . . . I heard from him (*Aet.* 15 and 16) that water contains a great amount of heat which does not make the water any hotter to the touch or to the thermometer; that this heat comes out of the water when it freezes and still the freezing water is not warmed by the escaping heat. . . . This appeared to me very

surprising; and still more astonishing did it appear that boiling water cannot be made any hotter by urging the fire. . . . These and similar things created in my youthful mind a vivid curiosity to know more of the science to which they appertained.[10]

Nevertheless, just as Eli Whitney had done, he drifted into the law when he graduated and, as was the custom in those days when there was no law school, studied in the New Haven office of Simeon Baldwin. At the same time, unable to tear himself away from his beloved college, he remained as tutor. In this way, he came to the notice of Dr. Timothy Dwight, Stiles's successor as president, and, just as he was admitted to the Connecticut bar, Dwight changed the whole course of his life.

What happened seems to us like a flagrant case of putting the cart before the horse. Yet it points very clearly to the newness, in America, of one branch of science and the primitive stage of its progress in the New World. Normally, nowadays, when a college picks a professor to fill a certain chair or to head a department, it searches for a person who knows the subject thoroughly, who can demonstrate his knowledge by the possession of a degree, and who has taught the subject for many years. But President Dwight of Yale College, after he had decided to establish a professorship of chemistry, did the opposite.

Young Silliman, twenty-two, met him on the campus

on a July day in 1801. Silliman told him of an opportunity he had to teach law in a Georgia university. Dr. Dwight shook his head.

"I advise you against it," he said in effect. "I have something to offer you here."

He then told Silliman about the chair of chemistry. Harvard had established such a professorship in 1783, and Dwight did not want Yale to stay too long behind Harvard. And then, to Silliman's amazement, he offered him the professorship!

"But I know nothing of chemistry! I know something of the law. But chemistry. . . ."

"We will see that you learn."

Then the president added—and Silliman later remembered his exact words:

"You will advance in the knowledge of your profession more rapidly than your pupils can follow you, and you will always be ahead of your pupils."

So Benjamin Silliman went to Philadelphia to learn the subject that he was to spend the rest of his life teaching and preaching.

Philadelphia was then the cultural center of the United States. A few years before—while the city of Washington was building—it had been the nation's capital. In it was the only important scientific society in the country—the American Philosophical Society established by Benjamin Franklin in 1743. To the university that Franklin also founded was attached a medical school in which chemistry was taught by such celebrated doctors as Benjamin

Rush and James Woodhouse. Here, too, was the scientist-inventor Robert Hare, who had designed the oxy-hydrogen blowpipe as a piece of laboratory equipment and with whom Silliman began a lifelong friendship. Hare also, in later years, became one of the most frequent and controversial contributors to Silliman's *Journal of Science*—writing articles that inspired many inventors.

Life in the large city was quite different from that in small, puritanical, churchly New Haven. Silliman was especially impressed by the rich food and wine served at the boarding house in which he lived—particularly when it gave him, as he thought, an acute case of gout. He was shocked, too, at the free thinking of some of the scientists with whom he associated. Woodhouse, whose lectures he attended regularly, disturbed him by never giving the Creator credit for the wonders of nature—something the deeply religious Silliman never failed to do. Perhaps that was a reason for his quiet glee at an incident that greatly embarrassed the doctor. Woodhouse had been lecturing on the lethal effect of hydrogen gas:

> It was stated that an animal confined in it would die; and a living hen was, for the experiment, immersed in the hydrogen gas with which a bell-glass was filled. The hen gasped, kicked, and lay still. "There gentlemen," said the Professor, "you see she is dead;" but no sooner had the words passed his lips, than the hen with a struggle overturned the bell-glass, and with a loud scream flew across the room, flapping the heads of the students with her wings while they were convulsed with laughter. The same thing might have occurred to any one who had incautiously

omitted to state that this gas is not poisonous, like carbonic acid, but kills, like water, by suffocation.[11]

Silliman was thus thinking ahead not of his pupils, as Dwight had prophesied, but of his teacher!

In the last months of his two-year preparation in Philadelphia, he began composing the lectures he would give in Yale. In some of the first of these he spread the gospels that had inspired James Watt.

> I enjoyed the important assistance of the lectures of the distinguished Dr. Black of Edinburgh, then recently published by his pupil and friend, Dr. Robison. This book was to me a mine of riches.[12]

His first tour of duty at Yale was short-lived. President Dwight's ideas about the teaching of chemistry were progressive. Like everyone else, he was pleased with the start Silliman made, but it was obvious that a profound understanding of chemistry could not be gained through lectures alone. A student truly dedicated to the study must be provided with the writings of the masters who, in Europe, had worked out the pattern of laws that had lifted chemistry out of alchemy, and he must also be given the means of experiment and proof—in short, a library and a laboratory. Silliman's experience in Philadelphia had introduced him to the books and, in the fascinating laboratory of Robert Hare—where indeed most of the equipment was of Hare's own invention and manufacture—he had learned what was needed for the experimental work. He had learned, too, that, except in the premises of such a genius as Hare, the instruments, furnaces, and utensils must come from abroad.

So the college corporation gave him more than a year's leave of absence, told him to go to England, Scotland, and parts of the Continent, gave him expense money, and told him to bring back the essentials. The story of his travels, which later ran through three editions —so hungry were Americans for every crumb of cultural information that might come from the Old World—is more fascinating than any travelogue of the period. Silliman was never too preoccupied with his job to enjoy every human encounter, every comic incident, every national weakness or virtue, every quirk of food or sport or language or way of life that was incidental to his journeys. In those easy-going days there was little specialization, and even such now complex matters as physics and chemistry were still part of the whole scene. In his book he tells not only of his intimate acquaintance with such leading scientific scholars as Humphry Davy, David Brewster, John Murray, and Thomas Hope but also of his being cheated by customs inspectors and booksellers, of his shrewd dealings with instrument makers, and of his conversations with chance acquaintances in hotels and on stage coaches and with University dons. On one occasion a Fellow of Cambridge University with whom he had spent the evening thought Silliman was having fun with him by pretending he was an American. "But," said the Cambridge man, "your English is no different from mine!" Everywhere he went, he found amazing ignorance of America among Englishmen, many of whom thought Americans spoke another language.

Silliman brought back not only the desired equipment for library and laboratory but also a fund of knowledge for his lectures. He was thus, in those sailing-ship and slow-communication days, one of the first bridges across the Atlantic over which scientific theory and practice, discovery and invention could travel from the centers of world culture to raw, young America.

From Murray and Hope in Scotland, he acquired a new interest in geology. He was able to use this in his lectures both in and outside the college. It led him to acquaintance with Colonel George Gibbs of Newport who owned the finest mineral collection in America and to obtain that collection for Yale. At the same time, soon after his return from abroad, he was instrumental in establishing the Yale Medical School whose first professor he became.

What the effect of Silliman's educational work might have been had he been provided with the facilities a professor of chemistry uses today can only be guessed at. But having provided the college with books and instruments, the corporation's generosity ended. Silliman never got a laboratory big enough for more than a handful of students to work in at a time. Advanced study was possible only for those he appointed as his laboratory assistants, and many of these, such as Denison Olmsted, James Dwight Dana, Edward Hitchcock, and Oliver Hubbard, became, in their generation, leaders of education in science. One laboratory assistant, Lyman Foot, who began work at the age of twelve, went on to become one of the army's principal surgeons.

In 1818, Silliman established the institution by which he best became known to posterity. This was the *American Journal of Science and Arts,* the only scientific periodical in the United States that has had an uninterrupted existence of more than a hundred and forty years. "Silliman's Journal" as it has always been called, became a sort of assembly line of scientific and technological information from all over the world. It was, too, for many years, the only American liaison between scientists and inventors.

The *Journal* was intended according to an announcement in its first number,

> to embrace the circle of the physical sciences, with their application to the arts, and to every useful purpose. . . .
>
> While science will be cherished *for its own sake,* and with a due respect for its own *inherent* dignity; it will also be employed as the handmaid to the arts. Its numerous applications to agriculture, the earliest and most important of them; to our manufactures both mechanical and chemical; and to our domestic economy will be carefully sought out, and faithfully made.[13]

The "arts" in 1818 meant, for most Americans, the mechanical as well as the fine arts. Yet Silliman's mental scope was so broad that, in his paper, he digressed, at times, into sculpture and painting. In the *Journal*'s first issue, for example, the leading article by Professor Alexander Fisher, was an essay on the "musical temperament." Other pieces in the first two volumes covered a wide variety of subjects. Copper, petrified wood, the connection between magnetism and light, the effects of earthquakes, the North Pole, icebergs, sponges off the shores of Long Island, the exoglossum, a new genus of fresh-water fish, Samuel Morey's revolving steam engine, the extraction of gelatine from bones, a theory of meteors, the origin of prairies, the manufacture of maple sugar, and the crystallization of snow were all dealt with there.

In the early years of the *Journal* it caught on slowly and was in constant financial difficulties. One reason for this was that Silliman was a perfectionist, insisting on the best rag paper, typography, and editorial care. Also, it carried no advertising. It never, indeed, made a profit. In a preface to the fiftieth volume in 1847 in which Silliman reviewed the *Journal*'s first thirty years, he wrote:

> It has been far from paying a reasonable editorial composition; often it has paid nothing, and at present it does little more than pay its bills. The number of engravings and the extra labor in printer's composition cause it to be an expensive work while its patronage is limited.
>
> It has a large gratuitous distribution, both at home and abroad. . . . Entire sets have often been presented gratuitously to our infant colleges and to scientific institutions and distinguished individuals in Europe.[14]

Obviously, its editor and publisher never thought of the *Journal* as a money-making enterprise but wholly as an educational one. As such, it reached ahead of every other periodical effort in the first half of the century.

The "patronage" may have been limited, but the *Journal* certainly went to the people who needed it most. Ingenious men and boys in every part of the growing nation—even on the frontiers—read every word of every issue, thumbing the pages until even the linen paper was dog-eared and ragged, searching for clues for the design of every sort of device from musical instruments to dynamos.

Here the American public was first informed of the parallel electromagnetic experiments of Michael Faraday in England and Joseph Henry in America, which told industrial inventors how to make giant magnets, to insulate wire, and to use induced currents. Here was a long, detailed account of how the inventor, Thomas Davenport, used the scientific teachings of Henry to make the first electric motor. Here, too, was an account of the first magnetic telegraph made by Joseph Henry to instruct the students of the Albany Academy, and of the intensity battery and intensity magnet Henry used to increase the distance capacity of that telegraph—information that was conveyed to Samuel Morse and that was essential to his success. The *Journal* also recorded the new developments of the steam engine and steamboat, lighter-than-air aerial navigation, and the system of interchangeable machine manufacture designed by Eli Whitney.

As the circulation of the *Journal* grew, there grew with it an enormous volume of correspondence. Every western explorer, every nature-lover, every amateur geologist, astronomer, or weather student whose curiosity was roused by an observation or discovery—whether it concerned insect life, fossils, celestial galaxies, or the mysterious underground oil that turned out to be petroleum—wrote a letter about it to Silliman. He read them all, published those that were worthy, and caused thereby a sort of chain reaction, for each letter produced a rash of others, controversial or amplifying, and we may find many a heated argument in the *Journal's* pages.

Silliman's way was not always easy. Ranged against his teachings of geology, for example, was the army of theologians whose fundamentalist convictions about the Old Testament were upset by the new revelations about the earth's creation. To Silliman, for all his deep religious faith, it was obvious that the geological phenomena he learned about were not the result of six days' effort even by the most omnipotent deity. But the fact that the developments in the earth's crust must have required countless thousands of years never disturbed him. He was able, in his own mind, to reconcile all this slow process with the existence of a Creator—much as today's liberal church people have done. But such was the prevailing mood of those days that it was only the constant reiteration of his religious belief that made it possible for him to continue his extracurricular lectures. To his audiences then, held by the spiritual aura in which he appeared to stand, his gospel of science carried through, but he was bitterly attacked in the press by the unconvinced clergy.

Financial worries were also at times frustrating. Most of these were in connection with his *Journal*. To carry it on over the lean years, he was obliged to make personal contributions. Fortunately, the great army of his devoted friends was able to help with the paper's support. And, in his later years, he was able to get lucrative work as a mining consultant, though the arduous travel by carriage, by river boat, and on horseback that this entailed would, but for his rugged constitution, have shortened his life.

After more than fifty years as professor, he retired and spent the remainder of his life relaxed and happy. He went again to Europe, where now he was known and admired. In his New Haven home he spent the greater part of his time arranging and revising his writings. Death came without suffering when he was eighty-four.

In his long lifetime, he had done more, perhaps, than anyone to build Yale from a small, narrow theological seminary to an institution that was recognized throughout the world as a center of liberal thought and original research. Surely he had established science there in a way that made it a fitting home for a man who has been thought the greatest scientist in American history, Josiah Willard Gibbs.

Under Silliman's aegis, the whole scientific climate of America altered. And the inventors here and abroad in whose background he stood are numberless by any estimate that history can make.

FOUR

Magnets for Inventors

It is certainly far from true that, because a small boy's pet rabbit ran away and he followed it into his first adventure, we now have the telegraph, the dynamo, the motor, and a host of other electrical inventions. Yet we cherish this story about Joseph Henry because it gives us an illumined glimpse into the boy mind of one of the greatest scientists in modern history and shows the first scene in the drama of his self-education.

The boy was living in Galway, New York, with his grandmother, and he held a job as all-round handy boy in the village store. In the afternoons, Broderick, the storekeeper, let him off to go to school. He learned little in school—just the rudiments of the "three R's"—and to him a book was a bore, something you had to have to take to school and to forget as soon as possible afterward.

One day when he was not working, a rabbit he was feeding jumped away from him and hopped down the village street. Joseph ran after it till it jumped into a hole in the foundation of a church. "Now," thought Joseph, "I've got you"—especially as he found the hole big enough to crawl into himself. But when he was inside, he forgot about the rabbit.

Overhead, light showed through a crack. Joseph

pushed at a board and it gave to his push, making an opening into a lighted room. Being exceedingly slender, the boy was able to lift himself through, and he found himself behind a bookcase. Cautiously, and feeling, perhaps, like a burglar, he worked his way to the front of the shelves, and on them were more books than he had ever seen. Nor were they schoolbooks: they were novels, volumes of essays and poetry, histories, and books of travel. Joseph took down a novel and began to read. He read till it got dark outside, and then he crept back through the cellar and ran home.

What he had found was the village library kept in the vestibule of the church. The libraries in such villages as Galway in 1809 were not extensive, and this one was evidently not much used because on the frequent visits Joseph Henry made to it through his clandestine entrance, he never met anyone. Eventually, however, he confessed to his boss the pleasure and excitement his little adventures had brought him, and Broderick, being an avid reader himself, arranged for the boy to go in by the door and even to take books home.

In itself, the incident seems insignificant—though we cannot help believing that, in the life story of so important a person, even the smallest details have meaning. And it is significant that Henry himself later recalled the event as a sort of curtain-raiser to his career. In the intellectual drought of the tiny village, it awakened in him a feverish thirst for knowledge of the world and of human behavior.

. . .

Joseph had been born in the city of Albany—some thirty-six miles east of Galway—in 1799. His father was a day laborer; his mother a beautiful woman with tastes above the life she was forced to live. Both were Scottish, the children of immigrants; they had arrived as youngsters on the same ship in June, 1775—the day before the Battle of Bunker Hill. Ann Henry was a Puritan, a devout Calvinist Presbyterian. William, her hardworking husband, died when Joseph was eight or so, and, apparently, she was so desperately poor that she could not keep the boy at home in Albany. So she sent him to live with his grandmother in Galway.

Broderick's store was the hangout for the village boys—as such places always are. We may suppose they sat on barrels, talked the little village gossip, and watched with interest the girls who walked by in studied aloofness. Of every group of boys Joseph seems to have been the center. He was handsome, well-built, and vivacious, full of new ideas and stories, and, even as a young boy, had a strong sense of the dramatic. He was, indeed, a wholly normal lad; there was nothing "long-haired" or eccentric about him, and he was easily the most popular boy of his age in town.

Curiously, the first talent he showed was not for the laboratory; it was for the theater. It is said that, but for an accident, he might have become an important actor. Such guesses, however, are hardly worth much attention; the accidents that do determine a man's career in the direction of his genius nearly always happen, and perhaps they are not accidents at all but a kind of secret working of the will. But in Joseph Henry's groping years of early adolescence, his dramatic interests seemed to dominate him. Inspired by his reading of fiction, he wrote plays, produced them, and acted in them; contrived ingenious stage sets and lighting; and organized a dramatic society.

At fourteen he was back in Albany, doing various jobs and going to night school at the Albany Academy, then a famous boys' school. Here his friends all thought of him as actor and playwright, showman and orator. In addition to his theatrical ventures, he had started a debating society, which he called "The Forum." He appeared to be wholly dedicated to public performance in an auditorium. Then, as he graduated, he startled his colleagues and admirers by announcing, in his valedictory address, that he was abandoning all his theatrical interests and embarking on a wholly different career. The fact was that the "accident" had intervened.

It happened when he was sixteen. A cold or some other minor sickness kept him a day or two at home and inactive. One of the boarders who helped Ann Henry keep body and soul together had left a book on the parlor table. Now any book left in the path of Joseph's restless mind was sure to be picked up and read. Joseph reached out for books in the same instinctive way that a hungry man reaches for food.

But his book was quite different from anything he had seen. There had been no such book in the Galway library. Even in the Academy, where there were text-books on mathematics, there had been no such thing as this. The title was *Lectures on Experimental Philosophy, Astronomy, and Chemistry.* It was, according to the author, an English clergyman named Gregory, "intended chiefly for the use of young persons." It opened with a series of questions.

> You throw a stone, or shoot an arrow into the air. . . . Why does it stop at a certain distance, and then return to you? . . . On the contrary, why does flame or smoke always mount upward, though no force is used to send them in that direction? And why should not the flame of a candle drop toward the floor when you reverse it instead of turning up and ascending into the air? . . . Again, you look into a clear well of water and see your own face and figure as if painted there. Why is this? You are told that it is done by reflection of light. But what is reflection of light? [15]

Here, repeated again and again was the one little word that is the springboard for every scientist's thought: WHY! Why this, why that. . . . Printed here the word caught the dormant scientist's mind in Joseph Henry and brought it suddenly, glowingly alive.

We have few details about this so-called accident, but we may imagine the owner of the book, a Scot named Robert Boyle, coming home after work to find the young man prone on the floor with his head buried in the little volume reading every word over and over in the fading light. We only know that Boyle was so amused and pleased by Joseph's interest that he immediately made him a present of the volume. And it remained in Henry's possession throughout his life.

> This book, [he wrote on the flyleaf in his mature years] by no means a profound work, has under Providence exerted a remarkable influence upon my mind. . . . It opened to me a new world of thought and enjoyment; fixed my attention upon the study of nature, and caused me to resolve at the time of reading it that I would immediately devote myself to the acquisition of knowledge.[16]

Science—or "philosophy" as it was then called—was in an exceedingly primitive state in the United States in the first decades of the nineteenth century. America could boast of only one truly great scientist in its two centuries of history, and Benjamin Franklin had lived most of his life in the colonial era. There had been a few great inventors by Henry's time—among them Eli Whitney and Oliver Evans, that pioneer in what we call automation—but none except Franklin who could compare with such deep thinkers about the laws of nature as Newton, Black, or Priestley; Laplace, Lavoisier, Ampère, Arago, Galvani, and Oersted. These men had worked all over Europe from Norway to the Mediterranean, and it was from Europe that Americans, in Henry's early years, got what science they had. While Henry was starting his career in an atmosphere of scientific ignorance with almost no facilities for experiment, his great English contemporary, Michael Faraday, whose electrical researches ran parallel to Henry's, worked in what was then in some ways the most civilized city in the world, London, and had the best of laboratories and equipment and the support of the celebrated Royal Society of England.

At the same time, the very absence of these perfect conditions was a spur to such a mind as Henry's. The difficulties in his way urged him toward achievement. The poverty that prevented him from buying the sort of materials that would have been ideal for his experiments forced him to find substitutes, and, in finding them, he made new discoveries.

Working sixteen hours a day, he perfected himself in mathematics, including calculus, and had time left for tutoring boys and for making many experiments of the sort that Joseph Black had tried with water, ice, and steam. When the late hours damaged his health, he got a job as surveyor, and the months in the open air so restored him and built up his physique that he never was ill again. The surveying job led to a far more important position as engineer for canal construction, but just at that moment a call came from the Albany Academy in which he had been educated. He was offered the chair of mathematics, and he accepted without question.

His unhesitating acceptance was characteristic. As engineer, he would have made far more money. Yet throughout his life, despite his poverty, money never held for him the least temptation. He was often criticized for this, for letting his many opportunities to enrich himself go to other men. But to Joseph Henry his mission was crystal clear from the moment he read Robert Boyle's little book. It was first to find the causes and the workings of natural law and then to give the knowledge he had gained for the enlightenment of mankind. There must be no restraint on his giving; he would give, give, give without pay or credit. This was his single passion, and when the professorship at the Academy was offered him, he saw with the intuition of genius that this would open the door to his desire.

Just before starting work at the Academy, Henry spent a few days in New York. One of his biographies has suggested that he may have gone there for relaxation—a last good time before he assumed his arduous duties in Albany—or, perhaps, simply for sightseeing. But Henry's idea of a good time differed from that of most young men. For him, there were more instructive things in the big city than the taverns or the theatres, and Joseph was seldom diverted from his passionate search for knowledge.

The New York sight that most stirred him was an electromagnet made by William Sturgeon of England— a prized possession of one of Henry's acquaintances. Sturgeon had designed this as a scientific experiment following the work of the European scientists, Oersted and Arago, who had shown a connection between magnetism and electricity. It was a bar of soft iron bent into the shape of a horseshoe and loosely wound with a spiral coil of bare copper wire. A coat of varnish insulated the iron from the wire. When the ends of the wire were attached to a galvanic battery, the horseshoe became magnetized; when they were detached, it lost its magnetism.

Henry took the memory of Sturgeon's magnet back to Albany with him, and it stayed in the back of his mind through his hours of lectures and teaching. His fingers itched to make an electromagnet of his own and improve, if possible, on Sturgeon's experiment. Most of all he wanted by the most exhaustive investigation to clarify the physical laws governing magnetization by galvanic current. But his work at the Academy left him no time. After his seven hours of lecturing on mathematics, physics, and chemistry—half of which were given to getting the fundamentals of arithmetic into the heads of the smaller boys—he must spend the rest of the day doing the jobs that take up all of a teacher's spare time: correcting papers, counseling individual students, and preparing the next day's lectures.

The young man, furthermore, had no place in which to work, no laboratory equipment provided by the school and not money enough to buy his own. The room in which he lectured contained only one long table for demonstrations and rows of wooden benches for the students. When Henry's lecture was finished, the room was immediately needed for other professors with their classes.

With these meager facilities, however, his teaching was distinguished and exceedingly popular. For one thing, he was a good showman. His theatrical experience had taught him how to make the most of a dramatic situation, and his often sensational demonstrations of chemical and physical phenomena held his students' attention. He would bring home, for instance, the effects of a galvanic current or static discharge by telling some thirty or more students to join hands and sending a shock through the line. He enjoyed the surprise of his classes at the bright sparks and loud cracks that animated his electrical demonstrations.

All of this talent for teaching kept Henry constantly in demand, and, for his own research, he was obliged to wait for the brief summer vacation when the boys would go home and the lecture hall would be empty.

The law governing the electromagnet was that a current from a battery running round an iron core at right angles to it would produce magnetism in the core. But, looking at Sturgeon's magnet with its spiral of wire, it was obvious that the current could not run at right angles to the iron of the horseshoe because the turns of the bare wire had to be slanted in order to keep apart and thus insulated from each other. Now the wire was insulated from the horseshoe by a coating of wax or varnish on the horseshoe. Was not, Henry wondered, some such treatment possible for the wire too? If the wire had some insulating covering, then the turns could be close together so that the right angle could be more nearly approached. Furthermore, coils of wire could be superimposed one upon the other.

It is said that Henry then appropriated his wife's silk petticoat, tore it into ribbons, and wound the ribbons round many feet of copper wire. (The same story is told of Thomas Davenport, inventor of the electric motor, but as Mrs. Davenport gave up her precious wedding dress for the sake of technological progress, her sacrifice was the greater. It is highly probable that both stories are true as any hurried quest for silk is likely to end in a lady's wardrobe.) Henry then wound his covered wire so closely that the turns touched. Immediately, the power of the magnet increased. He now wound a second coil over the first and obtained a further increase in power. It seemed as if the more wire the current went through—at right angles—the greater the magnetic force. Henry was not immediately sure of this, but his brilliant thought—which no one, apparently, had ever had—of insulating copper wire would assure a proof. Incidentally, he had shown the way to an invention that would be basic for all future applications of electric power.

He now came to a phase of his investigation that may have been prompted by his poverty. In Europe, such scientists as the great Faraday, working in well-equipped laboratories, were using large, expensive galvanic batteries for their electrical experiments—batteries containing many big plates of zinc and copper. Such things were rare in Albany, and to construct them would require an outlay far beyond the young teacher's means. But suppose, by a careful winding of more coils, he could get the same results as with a big battery . . . ! Following his hope, he made one of the most important series of experiments in the entire history of electrical investigation. Upon these and the discoveries to which they led, depend the dynamo, the motor, the transformer, and the telegraph, which are commonplace today.

He made his horseshoe of a bar of soft iron 20 inches long and 2 inches square. On it he wound, in close spirals, 540 feet of insulated copper wire in 9 coils of 60 feet each, letting the ends of the coils stick out from the horseshoe. He then tried letting a current run through various lengths of wire. A few excerpts from his own record of the experiment show his results.

Exp. 8. Each wire of the horse-shoe was soldered to the battery in succession, one at a time; the magnetism developed by each was just sufficient to support the weight of the armature, weighing 7 lbs.

Exp. 9. Two wires, one on each side of the horse-shoe, were attached; the weight lifted was 145 lbs. . . .

Exp. 14. When all the wires (nine in number) were attached, *the maximum weight lifted was 650 lbs.* and this astonishing result, it must be remembered, was produced by a battery containing only ⅖ of a square foot of zinc surface, and requiring only half a pint of dilute acid for its submersion.[17]

With a slightly different but not much larger battery he was finally able to lift 750 pounds, an achievement that was thought almost miraculous by the electrical experimenters of the day. As a final proof he attached the wires to a battery containing 28 plates (which he may have borrowed), and the lifting power was less!

While the larger battery was available, he made his discovery of quantity and intensity of magnetic force. Today we measure quantity with amperes and intensity with volts, but Henry knew nothing of such terms in 1830. His magnet of several short coils, which lifted the heavy weights when connected with a single pair of plates, he called a "quantity magnet." But he found that by using a single coil of wire instead of several short coils and connecting this with a large battery of pairs connected in series, the horseshoe became an "intensity magnet." With the increased voltage this gave, he was able to operate his magnet at a distance. The voltage he called "projectile force." And it was with such a magnet that he gave the dramatic demonstration his students never forgot, for it was, in truth, the first invention of the magnetic telegraph for which, unhappily, Samuel Morse has had all the credit.

He had come, in the summer, to know that his demonstration would work. So, when the boys came back, he first mystified them by stringing a mile of wire round the Albany lecture hall. Then he attached one end of the wire to the long coil round an intensity magnet. He then set a small iron bar on a pivot. One end was between the poles of the magnet. The other was an inch or so from a small bell on a stand. At the other end of the mile of wire he had his large battery ready. Giving the signal for silence, he connected his end of the wire with the battery through a mercury cup. Instantly the little bell rang. Then by repeatedly dipping his wire into the mercury he produced a series of ringing signals at the far end of the room.

Thus Henry had invented the telegraph a year before the idea occurred to Samuel Morse and five years before Morse, having constructed his telegraph, was puzzled because it would not work over more than a few feet of wire. It was, indeed, only after Henry's intensity magnet had been explained to him that he was able to construct a practical working model! Years later when Morse was reaping a small fortune from his patents, Henry's friends asked him why he had not taken advantage of his priority. He replied:

I did not then consider it compatible with the dignity of science to confine benefits which might be derived from it to the exclusive use of any individual.[18]

He did admit that "in this I was perhaps too fastidious," but he clung to his resolve throughout his life and let others reap rewards for their inventions based on his discoveries. When, for example, he constructed what was apparently the first electric motor ever made, he wrote:

Not much importance . . . is attached to the invention, since the article, in its present state, can only be considered a philosophical toy; although, in the progress of discovery and invention, it is not impossible that the same principle, or some modification of it on a more extended scale, may hereafter be applied to some useful purpose.[19]

And it was, indeed, only three years later that Thomas Davenport, working with precise replicas of the Henry magnets, made his first rotary electromagnetic motor.

From his experiments with magnets in 1831, Henry turned his attention to the great problem of induction. For several years, scientists in Europe had been puzzled by an idea that they believed must be true, though no experiment could prove it. If an electric current, they asked themselves, could produce magnetism, why could not magnetism produce an electric current?

Henry wound the armature (the iron bar that the horseshoe when magnetized attracted) with a coil of wire. Then he fastened the armature to the poles of an electromagnet. He attached the ends of the coiled wire to a galvanometer sensitive enough to register the slightest evidence of current. He then magnetized his electromagnet with a battery current. He observed that at the instant of sending the current through the magnet, the galvanometer needle moved—immediately going back to rest. When he broke the magnetizing current, the needle moved in the opposite direction. He had found, therefore, that a current was induced in the armature coil *only* at these two instants of making or breaking the magnetizing currents—a fact that had escaped the others. Here was the basis for the invention of every electric generator that has ever been built.

He next experimented with so-called "mutual induction," finding that a current in one wire may induce a current in the opposite direction in another—even one that is several hundred feet away. By showing that a current of high potential (he called it an "intensity" current) can be induced by one of low potential (quantity), he established the laws that govern today's transformer —which "steps up" or "steps down" a current—so essential in the transmission of power and its distribution. Without the application of these discoveries, the "juice" that moves the appliances in our homes could never enter our houses.

From mutual induction he went on to the most original discovery of all—self-induction. He found that when a current running through a long wire was interrupted, an opposing current was induced in the same wire. The induced current, therefore, retarded the primary current's progress. This caused difficulties when cables were first installed, but once the cause was known, devices could be invented to overcome the obstacle. So important was this discovery that the unit of induction was called the "henry." Thus Joseph Henry joined the scientists who had units named for them such as "volt," "ampere," "ohm," and "watt." This discovery led not only to inventions that overcame certain obstacles to cable communication but also to many other practical devices.

Working with what he called "common" (static) electricity from frictional electric machines or Leyden jars, he made the first experiments of electromagnetic waves. He showed that the discharge from a Leyden jar was "oscillatory," and by a dangerous demonstration during a thunderstorm found that lightning produced the same effect. Here was the dawn of radio: a first step in the long sequence of discovery and invention that led to Marconi and De Forest.

In the meantime, Henry had moved from Albany to Princeton, where he accepted a professorship in the then College of New Jersey—now Princeton University. Here with more leisure and better equipment he was able to carry on the brilliant researches that matured his earlier experiments. As at Albany, his teaching at Princeton drew crowds of enthusiastic students, who were constantly surprised by his demonstrations of powerful long-distance magnetism and electrical communication surpassing their farthest dreams.

His work at Princeton was so happy that one would expect him to stay there for the rest of his life. But his strong Calvinist conscience would not let him. He seems to have had an almost mystic sense of his mission—to do his utmost for the dissemination of scientific knowledge to all mankind. Thus when the Englishman, James Smithson, bequeathed an endowment "to found at Washington, under the name of the Smithsonian Institution, an establishment for the increase and diffusion of knowledge among men," Joseph Henry accepted the invitation to be its first secretary.

So, subordinating any impulse toward fame or even recognition for his work to the motive of encouraging other lesser scientists, he spent the rest of his long life organizing and administering this great American institution. It is an example of unselfishness exceedingly rare—perhaps unique—in the record of modern science. He lived long enough to see inventors all over the world profit by his discoveries, and, to him, the sense that he had inspired them—even when they did not know it or, like Morse, refused to admit it—was its own reward.

In England, the credit for many of Henry's discoveries goes to Michael Faraday, who made them independently. There has been much dispute on the wholly unimportant question of who was first. It seems to have been demonstrated that Henry's experiments with magnetism had priority, that he was the first to insulate wire, and that his discovery of self-induction was original.

But it must never be forgotten that while Faraday lived and worked in an atmosphere of deep scientific education in close communication with the scientists of Europe, Henry started from scratch in what was virtually a wilderness as far as scientific understanding or experience was concerned. Aided by the Royal Society of London, Faraday was able to use the expensive equipment given to the Society by Sir Humphry Davy, while Henry had to depend on his meager savings and the generosity of friends for his makeshift laboratories. Finally, while Faraday could give full time to his researches, Henry did not even have the leisure to publish the results of his experiments until long after Faraday had given his to the public. And communications were so slow and English periodicals so hard to obtain that Faraday's notices of his demonstrations never reached Henry until several years after his own had been concluded.

But Henry had only respect and admiration for his British colleague. On his sabbatical leave from Princeton, he sought out Faraday in England and the two became close friends.

As far as the world's scientific knowledge is concerned, the parallel work of these men is an excellent circumstance. That the same advances should be made by persons then so far apart raised the whole cultural level of the world. As for the United States, the work of Joseph Henry was of transcendent importance. It brought this country from its position far behind in the race of civilization almost into the van of useful study and established many of the bases for the tremendous growth of American industry in later years.

FIVE

Behind the Doctors

Near the town of Meissengott in Alsace a nine-year-old boy used to walk to school by a short cut off the main road. One day as he passed a patch of woods on this path a dog rushed out, attacked him, and threw him on the ground. The boy covered his face with his hands while the dog bit him several times on his body and covered him with foam from its mouth. A bricklayer, working on a nearby house, heard the child's cries and came to the rescue. He beat the dog off and picked up the boy, who ran home to his parents and told them the frightening story.

Joseph Meister's parents made instant inquiries, found that the dog had finally turned up at its master's house obviously mad and that his master had killed him. They then took little Joseph to Doctor Weber, their family physician, and asked his advice. The doctor cauterized the wounds and told them, in effect:

"This is all I can do. It is all that any physician can do. But there is a man in Paris who is not a physician but who knows more about rabies—or 'hydrophobia,' as they call it—than all the physicians in Europe. Take Joseph to him immediately. If anyone can save the boy, this chemist can do it."

But when Madame Meister came with her boy to the laboratory of this chemist, Louis Pasteur shook his head. The culture of virus that he had made from the brains of rabid dogs had, when they had been weakened or "attenuated" as he called it, been used to inoculate dogs that had already been bitten and these dogs had recovered. Again and again they had come back to perfect health. Pasteur was never satisfied with a few experiments; he must make a hundred before he would admit success. Now he was sure that he could prevent the development of rabies in dogs, providing he began his treatment in time and followed an exact procedure in his inoculations. But he had never inoculated a human being. Here, confronted by this desperate mother and her threatened boy, he was forced to the hardest decision of his life.

A less sensitive person would have been less disturbed. Many a physician—especially in those days when the medical profession was relatively in its infancy—would have regarded Joseph as just another patient who must take the consequences of his injury and its treatment. And a doctor who had been successful in so many experiments would hardly have hesitated.

But to Louis Pasteur every human being was an individual and his life was precious. The thought that this woman was putting the destiny of her child in his hands was deeply troubling to him. If Joseph had been his own son, Pasteur could have felt no greater concern for him. The fact that, in this his sixty-fourth year, the name of

Pasteur was a byword in every civilized country in the world never entered his mind as he contemplated the boy before him. But the story of Pasteur's fame had been told to Madame Meister and her faith was absolute.

As he stood in the office of his laboratory revolving the great question in his mind, the sound of dogs barking came from outside. More than two hundred dogs, sick and well, mad and sane, were in the laboratory. Whenever a mad dog was caught anywhere in France or even abroad, it was sent to the laboratory of Louis Pasteur. The mad dogs were isolated and closely observed in every phase of their illness. In another section lived the healthy dogs; dogs who had been inoculated again and again with the new serum. The place also swarmed with other animals: rabbits, guinea pigs, hens, and monkeys. Joseph Meister looked out the window at all these creatures in their pens and laughed at what he saw. Pasteur's voice breaking the long silence called him back.

"Yes, Madame Meister, I will do it. This won't hurt you much, Joseph."

"But is that all?" said Joseph as Pasteur withdrew the syringe. "We have come all this way for a little pin prick!"

"No, Joseph, you will stay here for a while. I'll give you a comfortable room to sleep in and there'll be a pin prick every day."

So Joseph spent his days visiting and talking to the animals and sleeping a long, healthy sleep at night. But

Pasteur did not sleep. As the inoculations increased in virulence according to the pattern worked out in hundreds of experiments, he became more and more anxious.

Pasteur [wrote his biographer who was also his son-in-law] was going through a succession of hopes, fears, anguish, and an ardent yearning to snatch little Meister from death; he could no longer work. At night, feverish visions came to him of this child whom he had seen playing in the garden, suffocating in the mad struggles of hydrophobia. . . . Vainly his experimental genius assured him that the virus of that most terrible of diseases was about to be vanquished, that humanity was about to be delivered from this dread horror—his human tenderness was stronger than all, his accustomed ready sympathy for the sufferings and anxieties of others was . . . centered in "the dear lad." [20]

But the end of the treatment came with Joseph still in perfect health; he went home at last to become famous as the first person in the world to be successfully inoculated against rabies after being bitten by a mad dog. From then on, men, women, and children came from all parts of Europe and even from America to take the treatment at the Institut Pasteur in Paris until, in our own day, there are branches of this institute in nearly every city.

The discovery of a vaccine against rabies came as the climax of a long career of usefulness. But can we think of Pasteur as one of the "scientists behind the inventors"? We are inclined to think of an invention as something mechanical or electrical. Yet the devices that have revolutionized medicine, surgery, and agriculture, that have wiped out the diseases that crippled the silk industry, the brewing industry, the manufacture of wine and vinegar, and the raising of sheep, cattle, hogs, and poultry are all true inventions. And the scientific discoveries of Louis Pasteur were behind all of these.

He grew up in the village of Arbois in the Department of Franche-Comté, where his father, a veteran of Napoleon's army, owned a tannery. In his boyhood, his intellectual power seemed dominated by his emotions. In school he was far from the top of his classes; his marks were little better than average.

Perhaps one reason for this was his teacher's annoyance at the boy's constant interruptions. It is said that the science master, driven one day to exasperation, exclaimed, "Who is teaching this class . . . you or I? It is my province to ask questions, not yours!" But his loyalties to his family and, from his earliest consciousness, to France were passionate. Indeed his affection for his parents and sisters and his devotion to his home actually retarded the progress of his education.

He wanted education—in science and mathematics especially—and wanted, early in his adolescence, to become a teacher. The goal of his ambition was the École Normale, the celebrated teacher's college of France. But when at fifteen, he went to Paris to a preparatory school for the great École, his homesickness was so acute that he had to abandon his project and go back to Arbois. This was an early foreshadowing of the conflict that endured in Pasteur as long as he lived, between his affections—his urgent emotional sensibilities—and the hard inexorable work that deep scientific research demanded of him.

It is interesting to the student of the creative mind that in this time of adjustment he worked continuously as an artist, making remarkable portraits of family and friends with pastel crayons.

As he grew older, science won out—at least over his almost pathological attachment to home. When he went again to Paris, he stayed. By this time the intense effort of his study was driving sentimental thoughts from his mind as long as books, chemicals, retorts, and a microscope were before him. Work became almost a part of his religion—work and the resolution that had overcome his nostalgia for home.

> To *will* is a great thing [he wrote to his sister] . . . for Action and Work usually follow Will, and almost always Work is accompanied by success. Those three things Will, Work, Success, fill human existence.[21]

By the time he was nineteen, he had learned the fundamentals of mathematics and physics—or what was known of those fundamentals in 1843—and in his twentieth year, he was admitted to the École Normale. From then on he grew more and more absorbed in chemistry. He moved from inorganic chemistry—then a well-explored field especially in France, where the work of Lavoisier had opened a whole new vista of understanding—into the chemistry of life, a realm still befogged by ignorance and superstition. The belief that a study of life processes in chemical terms was an affront to the Almighty was still current in the 1840's in many quarters. To Louis Pasteur, devout Catholic though he was, such a view was an affront to both human and divine intelligence.

We see him now at twenty, with his professorial beard and eyes that always seemed to be looking beyond the immediate scene, stabilized by work, haunting the libraries and laboratories of the École and the Sorbonne, listening with rapt attention to the lectures of his heroes, Jean-Baptiste Dumas and Antoine Jérôme Balard, living in a small room with a stone floor and a wood stove in the Latin Quarter, and taking long walks with his inseparable companion Charles Chappuis through the Luxembourg Gardens and the crooked streets of Left Bank Paris. Shyer, perhaps, than other young men of his age, more serious, yet subject to overwhelming enthusiasms, he had become, now that he had resolved his emotional problems, a thoroughly normal person but with almost superhuman energy.

It is so that we see him on one of the great days of his life running down the corridor from the laboratory, embracing the first person he met, shouting, "I have it, I have it," and pulling this startled acquaintance out into the garden to tell him the extraordinary story of his first great discovery.

What Pasteur "had" when he rushed out of the laboratory was something exceedingly technical; something that could scarcely be understood by anyone who was not a chemist. Fortunately, the man he so enthusiastically embraced was a member of the school's faculty and was able to see that an important scientific problem had been solved.

In those years, a new technique of chemical analysis was just beginning to dawn upon the eternally inquiring minds of the most astute of European chemists. This was crystallography: it brought chemistry and optics together. Its practice required the use of a microscope— always Pasteur's favorite instrument.

Certain chemical salts or compounds formed crystals that affected polarized light—light that has been reflected from a polished surface or that has passed through a prism—in various ways. Thus the crystals of one substance would turn a ray of polarized light to the right while the crystals of another would turn it to the left. The curious fact was that, according to the methods of analysis then known, the two substances were identical. They had the same composition, contained the same elements in the same proportion. Yet when the ray of light struck them, they behaved in a precisely opposite manner. So there must be a difference between them.

A German named Mitscherlich had done some experimenting with crystallography when suddenly he came upon a result that utterly bewildered him. He found that crystals formed by tartaric acid (a substance found in wine vats) turned polarized light to the right. What puzzled him, however, was that the crystals of an otherwise identical substance called racemic acid, also a by-product of fermentation, had no effect whatever upon the light ray. The ray went straight through the crystals without being deflected either to the right or to the left. This, to Mitscherlich, was a new phenomenon and one that, with all his study and experience, he could not account for.

When Pasteur heard of Mitscherlich's problem, he could think of nothing else. Working day after day and night after night with what racemic acid he could attain, with instruments that polarized light, and with a powerful microscope through which he could observe the tiny crystals, he finally hit upon the answer. Racemic acid salts contained tartaric acid crystals, which turned polarized light to the right, sure enough, but they also contained the crystals of another wholly undiscovered acid that turned it to the left. Pasteur proved the existence of this second acid by examining the crystals under a microscope. He found the tartaric crystals had little faces turned toward the right; the other's faces turned toward the left. The two acids, therefore, neutralized each other, so that the ray passed through the racemic acid in a perfectly straight line!

To the layman, this does not sound like a startling dis-

covery, but to the chemist it was transcendent. When it
became known that a student in his early twenties had
solved a problem that had baffled a celebrated German
chemist and, in solving it, had discovered a new acid,
some of the greatest scientists in France were interested.
Among them was Jean-Baptiste Biot, who was sceptical
till he had tried the experiment for himself, after which
he became one of Pasteur's greatest admirers and friends
and helped him in nearly every step of his career.

But to Pasteur, especially as he remembered it later,
the importance of the discovery lay not in its novelty or
in the revelation of a new acid but rather in the fact that
it was a first step in the direction of his long career—the
study of chemistry in its relation to the life processes.

It was only a half-conscious intuition that told Pasteur
that a living organism had somewhere, at some time,
been at work in the production of these acids—both by-
products of wine and beer-making processes. But he
knew he must keep on experimenting with racemic acid.
Unfortunately, this substance was exceedingly rare. With
the stubborn persistence that was so characteristic of
him, he traveled all over Europe, hunting for this chemical whose crystals would not deflect the light ray. His
friends compared this hunt with the search for the Holy
Grail; it was so utterly dedicated, so seemingly divinely
inspired. "Never," said a contemporary newspaper story,
"was treasure sought, never adored beauty pursued over
hill and vale with greater ardour." But he could not find

enough acid for his experiments, so he worked out a way to make it synthetically. He thus became one of the pioneers in synthetic organic chemistry. Having in this way obtained enough for long experimentation, he came to the next step in his march toward the world of microorganisms, of life in its smallest forms. This world, to him, was one of beauty, adventure, and a pattern not unlike that of the jungle or even of human society with armies fighting each other: the conflict, as it were, of good and evil, with triumphs and defeats. His desire that the constructive organisms should triumph over the destructive ones seems somehow allied with his intense desire that the France he so loved should vanquish her enemies!

One day he found that a blue mold whose Latin name was *penicillium glaucum*—the sort of thing that forms over stale bread or cheese—had an extraordinary effect on his racemic acid. It destroyed the crystals that turned polarized light to the right and had no effect on those that turned it to the left. Now this mold was, definitely, a living plant with destructive power. It was this discovery that opened the door upon that vast society of microscopic beings that he now believed must have contact with all animal and plant bodies and that wrought havoc with so many of them.

The focus of his study now became the culture of the various organisms he had come to believe in until they formed large, powerful masses. He then manipulated them so that they would fight one another with constructive results. But he knew that the hit-or-miss practice, the trial-and-error experiments that were going on in agriculture, husbandry, and medicine and in the industries that dealt with organic materials, would never get anywhere until scientists established basic laws for the various inventors to base their work on. "Without theory," he said, "practice is but routine born of habit. Theory alone can bring forth and develop the spirit of invention."

Now one of the unscientific practices that he saw going on in France was taking place in the manufacture of wine—then, as now, one of the principal French industries. A great part of the wine produced—the very best wine over whose making the most careful known techniques were practiced—was wasted. In spite of the precautions, it turned bad. What was really happening, Pasteur thought, was that the process of putrefaction was following that of fermentation. Now both these processes, he believed, were produced by tiny organisms —living, wriggling, eating, and reproducing beings perfectly visible under the microscope. By long observation, he was able to distinguish the germs of fermentation and those of putrefaction. As long as the wine was fermenting, these showed as round globules; the moment it began to putrefy (or "go bad") the globules were replaced by elongated forms.

Now there was a persistent belief among scientists and physicians everywhere in what was called "spontaneous generation." It was thought that this was the cause of disease and decay in plants, animals, and men.

Something suddenly happened inside the organism—having no external cause—that produced deterioration, putrefaction, fevers, or the breakdown of tissue. Even fermentation and the later souring of wine or beer was thought to occur because something suddenly became alive within it—something that had no discoverable origin except in "nature." From the first Pasteur sensed this theory to be false. Every germ must come, he believed, from some other germ. And the germ entered from without: it was not born inside the body in which it grew. The greater part of his life was devoted to combating the theory of spontaneous generation, and the fight made many enemies. But Pasteur cared little about this as long as he knew he was approaching truth. Truth with a capital letter was Pasteur's ultimate goal in everything he did.

Pasteur's microscope, then, detected two kinds of microorganisms: the globular one, which caused fermentation, came in the yeast that converted the grape sugars into alcohol. This organism lived without air. The second with its elongated form, which must have free oxygen to live, came into the wine or beer from the atmosphere. It was important, therefore, as soon as fermentation was complete to kill the germs—the putrefaction germs—that came into the wine from the air. Pasteur found he could do this by heating the liquid to a certain temperature (about 120° F.). Thus began the famous process known as *pasteurization* applied by law to American milk and ever since Pasteur's day to the wine and beer of France. The first effect in Pasteur's lifetime was to revolutionize the French wine industry and to put a failing business on a new basis of prosperity. This was done by the industrial inventors behind whom stood Pasteur's pure research.

Although he was obliged to fight every inch of the way against ancient traditional prejudices and taboos, the results in thousands of cases were so obvious that Pasteur's popularity as well as his celebrity began. After his successes with wine he was hailed not only as a scientific genius but also as the savior of the national economy.

Because of his new fame among industrialists, he was led from chemistry and bacteriology into biology. One of the great French industries was the making of silk from thread spun from the cocoons in which a silkworm became a moth. Suddenly a disease spread in the *magnaneries* or nurseries in which the worms were cultivated, and the worms died by millions or their cocoons became useless. Every sort of treatment was given to the worms, whose symptoms appeared as tiny spots, but without result. Because of the minute size of the spots (or corpuscles) the disease was called *pebriné,* the peasant word for "peppered." Pasteur was called in and, greatly moved by the devastation the disease had caused, dropped everything else to study it.

The prosperity of an entire French region had been

wiped out. In the introduction to his book on silkworm disease, Pasteur wrote:

> A traveller coming back to the Cevennes mountains after an absence of fifteen years would be saddened to see the change wrought in that countryside within such a short time. Formerly he might have seen robust men breaking up the rock to build terraces . . . then planting mulberry trees [on which the silkworm fed] on these terraces. These men in spite of their hard work, were then bright and happy, for ease and contentment reigned in their homes.
>
> Now the mulberry plantations are abandoned, the "golden tree" no longer enriches the country, faces once beaming with health and humour are now sad and drawn. Distress and hunger have succeeded to comfort and happiness.[22]

Naturally the patriotic Pasteur was deeply moved to see a part of his beloved France thus turned into desert. Immediately he collected large quantities of worms, eggs (called seed), and moths and examined them under his microscope. He made his own silkworm nursery or *magnanerie* and watched the growth of the worms, the building of the cocoons, the emergence of the moths. As these processes took time, his study stretched over the years.

There were many puzzling circumstances. Sometimes perfectly healthy worms would hatch out of a batch of seed and the spots never appear until the moth came out of the chrysalis. But then that moth would lay diseased eggs. These paradoxes harassed Pasteur, kept him awake at night, and finally, along with other problems, broke him to a point at which his life was despaired of. From a stroke or lesion in the cerebral cortex, his entire left side was paralyzed. In Paris, to which he had returned from the Cevennes country, he lay, day after day, in his bed while the great men of France came to visit him. Yet his mind remained clear and he was able to dictate to his wife notes and papers on his researches. Finally—very likely, perhaps, by that Will in which he had such trust—he was able to get up and walk slowly, painfully, and with great consequent fatigue. "Now," he said, still feeble, still pitifully weak, "I must go back to my worms. France must not suffer from my weakness. A man's life is worthless if it is not useful to others." His friends and family fought his decision, but nothing would sway him. That he was saved at last and restored to health was thought by many to be a miracle.

Bit by bit he came to the conclusion that the *pebriné* was a hereditary disease. In order to be certain of its existence, there must be microscopic examination not merely of the eggs, the worms, and the cocoons, but also of the moth. It was in the moth alone that the spots invariably appeared if the disease was present in the strain. So the answer was to work by selection: to use only eggs laid by a disease-free moth and destroy all others. This was difficult because of the sale of tainted eggs by unscrupulous "seed" merchants, but once the "inventors" so to speak—the industrial technicians— became convinced enough to apply Pasteur's theoretical formulas, the silk industry, like the wine and beer industries, was restored to prosperity.

The system he evolved for the elimination of the hereditary *pebriné* disease was, according to Vallery-Radot, his biographer,

> quite simple; at the moment when the moths leave their cocoons and mate with each other, the cultivator separates them and places each female on a little square of linen where it lays its eggs. The moth is afterwards pinned up in a corner of the same square of linen, where it gradually dries up; later on, in autumn or even in winter, the withered moth is moistened in a little water, pounded in a mortar, and the paste examined with a microscope. If the least trace of corpuscles appears the linen is burnt together with the seed which would have perpetuated the disease.[23]

Thus far, Pasteur had not concerned himself with the diseases of the higher animals—though he was reasonably sure that they too were carried by "infinitesimally small" organisms that were capable of rapid reproduction. Meanwhile, he had lived a rich personal life, not all of it happy. From his student days, he had kept close touch with his father and sisters, sending them detailed reports of his work. It is, indeed, from this family correspondence that we know so much about him. He had married the daughter of an educator—herself uncommonly educated—who was a true partner in his work. She had borne him a son and three daughters. Typhoid fever (toward the reduction of which Pasteur later led the way) had taken the lives of two of the girls.

He had been continually harassed by his scientific adversaries, who persistently ridiculed his belief in disease microbes. He was forever under attack by physicians who called him a "mere chemist" who ought to keep out of their province. Yet at the same time he had staunch supporters who thought he was wasting time answering the attacks, and he had been honored by government awards including the Legion of Honor and had been elected to the Institute.

Among his admirers were the farmers. When the diseases of anthrax, swine fever, and poultry cholera became epidemic among the beasts on whom their living depended, it was inevitable that Pasteur should be called in.

In some seven French provinces where sheep were raised on a large scale, a mysterious disease called *charbon* or splenic fever (now known as anthrax) was causing death in a large percentage of every flock each year. Its effect was nearly always fatal; the animals, after symptoms of weakness, palsy, and shortness of breath, died in a few hours. Furthermore, in many cases the disease had been transferred to shepherds apparently through cuts or skin breaks. Thus another menace of ruin hung over Pasteur's beloved country, and he was quick to respond to the call.

Certain veterinarians had observed microscopic organisms in the form of tiny cylindrical rods in the blood of diseased animals but had regarded these merely as curiosities. A few had believed them to be virulent bacteria, but they were ridiculed by other doctors who had strong anti-microbe convictions and were finally convinced by experiments performed by the sceptics that their theories were fallacious and that the disease was caused by an inanimate substance in the blood.

Pasteur quickly exposed the carelessness with which these experiments had been conducted and proceeded to some experiments of his own. A tiny drop of infected blood was placed in a broth in which the bacteria could reproduce; after a few hours a drop of liquid from this medium into which the blood had been dropped was put into a second vessel of broth with no new addition of blood, then a drop from that into a third and so on to the fortieth flask. Then from that fortieth flask after all this dilution, a drop injected under the skin of a rabbit produced virulent disease! Thus Pasteur conclusively proved that the infecting agent could not be an inanimate thing but a living creature that reproduced itself in every dilution. His report stated that

> one single germ of bacteridium in the drop which is sown multiplies during the following hours and ends by filling the whole liquid with such a thickness of bacteridia that, to the naked eye, it seems that carded cotton has been mixed with the broth.[24]

This conclusive result has been defined by a Pasteur pupil named Chamberland in these words:

> By his admirable process of culture . . . Pasteur shows that the rods which exist in the blood, and for which he has preserved the name of bacteridia . . . are living be-

ings capable of being indefinitely reproduced in appropriate liquids, after the manner of a plant multiplied by successive cuttings.[25]

Having proved to his own satisfaction—and Pasteur was hard to satisfy even after hundreds of experiments —that this contagious disease was carried by bacteria or microbes, he persuaded the sheep farmers to take all kinds of safety measures such as the burying of dead sheep in places not used by live sheep for grazing and by the many rules of cleanliness that showed Pasteur was well advanced on the road to asepsis. But no sooner was the sheep disease well under control than he was called to the country of poultry farms to investigate a disease known as chicken cholera and then to work on the hog disease of swine fever. And it was here that he evolved what is usually thought the most revolutionary achievement of his career.

Vaccine against smallpox had been successfully used since the seventeenth century. It was known and approved in America by Cotton Mather and Benjamin Franklin. But no one knew *why* it was effective or had the faintest understanding of its bacteriological significance. In his work on animal diseases Pasteur now inquired into the reasons for immunity through innoculation.

He found that by "attenuating" the microbes he could produce what we now call a serum for causing protection from many virus diseases. There were various methods of attenuation: starving, excessive contact with oxygen, or heat treatment of the cultures. He finally arrived at the point where by injecting the serum in doses of increasing virulence over a period of time he could completely immunize animals against anthrax, chicken cholera, and swine fever, and he was becoming reasonably certain that the same treatment would protect human beings against the terrible scourges of the so-called incurable virus maladies. He was coming then, step by step, to that triumph for which he was most celebrated—the protection against the bites of mad dogs.

It seems incredible to us that, less than a hundred years ago, conditions existed in hospitals all over the world that were simply the result of unclean surgery. Sterilization was virtually unknown, and the need of it was only guessed at by such geniuses as Lister in England and Pasteur in France and a few of the disciples of these men. Instruments were used on patient after patient, merely washed between operations; bandages and dressings were made from hospital sheets that were crawling with bacteria. Surgeons did not even wash their hands with any thoroughness before operating. The result was that a majority of those who underwent major operations died in agony from gangrene, septicemia, or purulent infection. The atmosphere of the hospitals, instead of smelling of clean disinfectants, was fetid with the odor of suppurating wounds.

But in England, Lister was beginning the practice of

antisepsis—the killing of germs with alcohol or carbolic acid—while Pasteur, in France, was working on asepsis or protection of wounds from infection by airborne germs and the sterilization of instruments and dressings by heat. Even in his work on animals, Pasteur had always passed every knife or lancet through flame before using it. His very first belief about microorganisms—including those that affected beer and wine—had been that most of them had their existence in what he called the "dusts" of the air.

But both Lister and Pasteur found it necessary to fight continuously against obstinate ignorance and such traditional theories as that of spontaneous generation. This, however, has been the fate of most pioneer scientists whose unceasing, patient, gruelling experimental work had carried them far beyond the understanding of their contemporaries.

Yet in time, inventors followed Pasteur as they had followed the discoverers of thermodynamic and electromagnetic laws. Surgeons and hospital administrators devised new techniques, medical suppliers new sterilizing equipment, laboratory men better microscopes and other laboratory tools. Entirely new agricultural methods were devised. Food processors, canners, bottlers made new machines for avoiding air contact, and equipment was designed for the large-scale "pasteurization" of wine and milk. And, with all this new technology, with a saving of lives and suffering undreamed of before his time, it seems as if the whole aspect of civilized society had changed during the half century of Pasteur's active career.

Those who have explored Pasteur's life—and we think especially of the man who married his daughter, Doctor René Vallery-Radot—see always a division in his character between the scientist and the humanitarian. Intensely affected by suffering, he did everything he could to avoid inflicting pain even on the dogs with which he was experimenting. He would not vivisect a dog, for example, without anaesthesia—a technique rarely practiced by contemporary experimenters. When one of his treatments to prevent hydrophobia in a child who had been bitten failed because she had not taken it in time, he is said to have burst into tears. When he visited hospitals, the conditions he saw recurred to him in nightmares and visions that kept sleep away.

When the Franco-Prussian War came in 1870, he tried, forgetting the stroke from which he had barely recovered, to enlist in the French army. His bitterness against the Prussian "aggressor," as he believed him to be, never quite left him. The satisfaction he derived from his achievements came entirely from his sense that they redounded to the glory of *La Patrie,* France. Perhaps he never realized that the billions of francs he saved his fatherland exceeded the billions of reparations paid to Germany after the war—a fact that was brought out by Thomas Huxley.

In one of his last speeches, Pasteur expressed a thought that is far more alive today than when he spoke in 1888.

If I might be allowed [he said] . . . to conclude by a philosophical remark . . . I should say that two contrary laws seem to be wrestling with each other nowadays; the one, a law of blood and of death, even imagining new means of destruction and forcing nations to be constantly ready for the battlefield—the other, a law of peace, work and health, ever evolving new means of delivering man from the scourges that beset him.

The one seeks violent conquests, the other the relief of humanity. The latter places one human life above any victory; while the former would sacrifice hundreds and thousands of lives to the ambition of one. The law of which we are the instruments seeks, even in the midst of carnage, to cure the sanguinary ills of the laws of war; the treatment inspired by our antiseptic methods may preserve thousands of soldiers. Which of those two laws will ultimately prevail, God alone knows. But we may assert that French science will have tried, by obeying the law of Humanity, to extend the frontiers of Life.[26]

And, in another address, a funeral oration to one of his heroes, he gave expression to his faith in these words:

Blessed is he who carries within himself a God, an ideal, and who obeys it: ideal of art, ideal of science, ideal of the gospel virtues, therein lie the springs of great thoughts and great actions; they all reflect light from the Infinite.[27]

In every instant of his life: in his schools, in his laboratories, in the halls of the great Académie Francaise, and in his home, Louis Pasteur kept that faith.

Scientist Behind Himself

A fifteen-year-old boy arriving in New York as an immigrant, speaking no English, with no American relatives or friends and with only five cents in his pocket, does not suggest a promise for the future of American science. Today before such a lad could set out for this country, he would need to have an American sponsor. But the immigration laws were less severe in 1874. In that day when the gates of the United States were open to all of Europe, jobs were still available to penniless foreigners. So, after the officials had talked to him in German and found him a more than usually intelligent boy, young Michael Idvorsky Pupin was permitted to enter the great whirlpool of lower Broadway.

His welcome to the "land of opportunity," as the United States was known all over the world, was not calculated to inspire confidence. The first sight that attracted him was that of a woman selling pies and, seeing in her display his favorite of all sweets—a prune pie —he gave her his one nickel and got in return a pastry filled not with prunes but only the pits of prunes! But Michael merely laughed at himself for the trick that had been played on him, and the words of a fellow passenger in the steerage of the *Westphalia* came sharply back to him: "No matter who you are or what you know or what you have you will be a greenhorn when you land in America." In the next few years he applied the term cheerfully to himself and made up his mind that he must serve his "apprenticeship as a greenhorn" before he could become a real American.

His first thought when he was planning to escape from Europe was not to become an American. He was immensely proud of his Serbian ancestry and intensely nationalistic in his rebellion against the empire of Austria-Hungary into which his native land had been absorbed. But he chafed under the restrictions imposed by the caste pattern in which he grew up. He could see no future in Europe to reward the work of his restless, far-reaching mind. Before he was in his teens, he had felt the conflict between the story of Benjamin Franklin's kite and the superstitions taught him by the schoolteacher and the "wise men" of his home village of Idvor—a place that Pupin later said was on no map. In his mind the boy had followed Franklin to America, the land that Franklin had helped set free, and then his imagination had jumped to Lincoln who had helped maintain its freedom, and the two became his heroes. Thus were set in his very early years the twin interests of his life: science and political philosophy. In spite of living in an oppressed community and being taught the tales of soothsayers, his inquiring mind sought scientific truth and his rebellious heart yearned for freedom. Franklin and Lincoln seemed the answers to both.

Yet there were lessons he learned in his early boyhood at home that stayed with him throughout his life. The boys of Idvor did night duty watching the cattle in the big pastures. At the approach of cattle thieves, or when any disturbance occurred, the boys who watched wide apart had a system of signaling. A staff with a knife in the end was plunged in the earth. When the staff was struck, the sound would carry far through the ground to a remote boy who was listening. The memory of this was to lead the mature Pupin to his most celebrated achievement.

Michael's exuberant spirit soon burst the confines of Idvor, and, on the threshold of his teens, he moved to Prague in Bohemia. Prague, like Idvor, was part of the hated empire. There he found the same insurgency among the Slavic people as in his native province of Banat (now in Yugoslavia), and Michael's patriotic activities with the Bohemian rebels interrupted his studies and troubled his conscience. He felt that the expense of the school, which was being borne by his parents back in Idvor, was not justified. Then when he heard of his father's death and knew that his widowed mother would have to bear the full cost of his education, he made the decision that changed his life.

He would go to the country of his heroes, the land of infinite opportunity. There he would be free from revolutionary temptations and from the limitations of the peasant class into which he had been born. *There, too, he would make his fortune.* In a few years, he would return with wealth and glory to the homeland, where he would enrich his family and help again in the fight for freedom.

By the sale of nearly every possession, he scraped up enough money for his passage in the steerage of the *Westphalia.* He left Hamburg with little more than the clothes he was wearing. He had even sold his overcoat. The hardships he suffered on that transatlantic voyage would have killed many a migrating adolescent. He kept warm by hugging the steamer's smokestack. He slept without mattress or blanket. Fortunately, the open air life of his peasant childhood had given him an exceedingly rugged physique, and he arrived in good shape for the hard fight ahead.

Michael's was not an unusual dream for a southern European youth in the 1870's. They came to America in those days by the hundred thousand, all with high hopes. The singular fact in Pupin's case was that the dream, in large part, came true. He not only earned a fortune, but his scientific contribution to his adopted land changed the face of the country.

He wrote his story at last—the story of the nickel that was multiplied many million times in a mixed climate of pure and applied science—in a book called *From Immigrant to Inventor.* There are few more inspiring narratives in American literature.

Michael Pupin called himself an inventor, but he was far more. Invention was not his profession. The great achievement in applied science that made his fortune was a by-product of his work as a scientific investigator. He was, in himself, a sort of bridge between scientist and inventor. He was the scientist behind his own inventions. But he also, by his teaching, inspired other inventors.

He could not approach science in the direct way that more fortunate men have done: Josiah Willard Gibbs, for example, or Louis Agassiz. Before he could complete his education, he had to finish his "apprenticeship as a greenhorn," taking whatever jobs presented themselves. He drove mules on a Delaware farm, worked as a journeyman painter and paper hanger in New York City, cultivated corn and tobacco fields in Maryland, and, again in Manhattan, shoveled coal from wagons into cellars and then worked his way up to foreman in a cracker factory near New York's Bowery. Yet at every step of the way he was educating himself to be both an American and a scientist. And he seems to have collected a set of ideals that eventually crystallized into the goals of his life.

A girl on the Delaware farm supplemented his sketchy knowledge of American history by adding George Washington to his symbols of Franklin and Lincoln, but she also imbued him with a sense of American democracy, which proved to him that he could not go back to an old-world way of life. In his wanderings from job to job, he passed through Princeton, New Jersey, and was overwhelmed by the academic atmosphere there. He got into conversation with a Princeton undergraduate in front of Nassau Hall, and from then on Nassau Hall was a symbol of his yearning for education. Close by the New York cracker factory was Cooper Union, in whose free reading room he spent all of his spare time devouring the books that satisfied his hunger for understanding of physics, mathematics, and the laws of nature. And in the cracker factory itself, he was fascinated by the boiler room and the steam engine that ran the machines.

The first questions that presented themselves to him had been concerned with light, sound, and heat.

> The first ideas of sound and light [he wrote] I caught on the pasturelands of my native village; the first ideas of the phenomena of heat I caught in the boiler-room in Cortlandt Street and at Cooper Union lectures.[28]

But he noticed a striking difference between the attitude toward physics in the United States and that in the Europe he knew. The Americans, for example, were chiefly concerned with "what heat can do and not what it is." Pupin's own "Slavonic craving" was to know "what heat is." In a visit to the centennial exposition at Philadelphia he had observed that

> All scientific efforts exhibited there concerned themselves with the question of what things can do, rather than what they are.[29]

Perhaps no one has ever expressed more simply and clearly the American feeling about science in the nineteenth century.

.   .   .

After five American years Michael Pupin was sure he had finished his initiation.

> No longer a greenhorn! [he wrote some fifty years later].
> Oh what a confidence that gives to a foreign-born youth
> who has experienced the hardships of serving his appren-
> ticeship as a greenhorn! Then there were other sources of
> confidence: I had a goodly deposit in the Union Dime Sav-
> ings Bank and it was several thousand times as big as the
> nickel which I brought to Castle Garden when I landed.
> Besides, I had learned a thing or two in the evening classes
> at Cooper Union, and my English was considered good
> not only in vocabulary and grammer, but also in articula-
> tion . . .[30]

By this time he had come to love New York so much that he transferred the symbol of Nassau Hall to Colum-bia College. He had taken to going to church in Brook-lyn to hear the sermons of Henry Ward Beecher; not be-cause his religion had changed from the Orthodox creed of his Serbian childhood but because this famous preach-er's sermons appealed to his intelligence. Through a friend he made at church he was introduced to Adelphi Academy in Brooklyn, and there he prepared for the entrance examinations to Columbia. In all this time, he was enjoying life exuberantly, making friends every-where, and purging the Serbian idioms from his speech. The hard work of study did not divert him from rec-reation or from attention to his physical health and muscular development. When an interscholastic contest

113

was scheduled, he volunteered to run in a ten-mile race for which he had had no previous training. He won!

> From that day on my friends at the Adelphi Academy regarded me as one of their number, and it was a liberal education to me to listen to their eulogies of *my loyalty to them and to their institution,* which they said, I displayed when I fought under the Adelphi banner on the athletic field.[31]

Pupin underlined this bit about "loyalty" because such a sentiment about an educational institution was entirely new to him—as it would be to any European, accustomed to schools in which nothing is as important as scholastic achievement. Yet the idea did not repel him; it delighted him; and when he entered the freshman class at Columbia, he rejoiced in the American scheme of combining athletics and other extracurricular activities with study.

His strenuous life on Delaware and New Jersey farms following an outdoor boyhood had so toughened him that he was more than a match for the city boys. He easily beat them at boxing and wrestling, and he was amused at the prestige his victories gained him. He observed that his classmates were puzzled, however, at his high marks in spite of his enthusiastic interest in sport and other out-of-class indulgences. What he was never quite able to understand was his growing popularity. Why, when he reached his junior year, he was elected president of his class over candidates from the oldest, most aristocratic (as he supposed) New York families—especially as he had never wholly rid himself of a foreign inflection and obviously hailed from so outlandish a part of the world—was a question that continued to puzzle him.

Pupin had not entered college with the special intent of devoting himself to the study of scientific subjects. His educational interests seem to have been spread over a wide field. One was the classics of antiquity and the history of Greece and Rome in the pre-Christian era. For his full enjoyment of this, he had perfected his reading of Greek and Latin; he had learned by heart long passages in the original from the *Odyssey,* the *Iliad,* and the *Aeneid.* From listening to the illiterate ballad singers of his native land who carried the Slavic history from generation to generation by word of mouth, he had acquired a passionate love of poetry. This later combined with his attachment to pure science, so that he spoke of the great discoveries of Newton, Faraday, and Maxwell as "poems." To him, to demonstrate a theory in physics was to compose a poem!

Yet even when he worked at Columbia for his broad education, his turning point had come. In the life of nearly every great scientist, there is such a point. We saw it in the adolescence of Joseph Henry when he found the little book on "natural philosophy." In Pupin's case, he had stumbled on two volumes in the Cooper Union library while he was still working in the cracker factory. One was the printed lectures on heat, sound, and light delivered in America by John Tyndall at the moment that Michael had been driving mules in Delaware. The other was *The Poetry of Science* by Robert Hunt. The effect of this reading may have been subconscious at the time, but certainly the books were seeds destined to grow into a career. And there can be no doubt that they were more exciting to the boy than any novel could have been.

In the years that followed Columbia, we see those seeds growing in a climate in which wonder, mysticism, hero-worship, and indomitable will were curiously blended with normal, human, pleasure-loving desires. Columbia professors, impressed by his earnestness, gave him letters to important teachers in Cambridge University, then the principal center of mathematics and physics in England. Before taking up his studies, he paid a visit to Idvor. His mother, who could neither read nor write, seems to have had a kind of psychic intuition and a deep spiritual understanding. She inspired the mystic approach to the traditions he was to know in England, for she called those new heroes of his, Bacon, Copernicus, Newton, Faraday, and Maxwell—the "saints of science" and Cambridge, of which she knew only what her son told her—"the great temple consecrated to the *eternal truth."*

In Cambridge, he was assigned to a class of students who were aspiring to honors in mathematics. Though he worked there under a celebrated teacher, he was soon discontented and his restlessness produced a decision of profound importance. The mathematical problems were masterpieces of ingenious complexity, but, he thought, they are tricks. If you worked out the solutions to the puzzles, you were a clever fellow and entitled to honors, but there was the end of it. There was nothing creative in that. The work was not leading to new, original discovery but only made a student capable of passing a tough examination. Mathematics was useful, sure enough, as a tool with which to work in physics, but, as it was taught in Cambridge, Pupin thought it was regarded as an end in itself. His insistently querying mind wanted to get at the nature of things—of matter, of forces, of counterforces—not merely to find out how they worked. His fingers itched to handle laboratory equipment: balances, instruments of measurement, sources of electricity and magnetism so that he might explore the essential structure of scientific truth and, perhaps, discover some hidden law as Newton, Faraday, and James Clerk Maxwell had done.

The world at that time—in the late 1880's—was on the threshold of a revolution in its understanding of natural phenomena. Much research, often following false hypotheses, had brought it to that threshold. For the first time since Newton, men here and there were beginning to doubt beliefs that had seemed infallible for the greater part of the century. Curious things were going on in the laboratories, events that suddenly threw accepted theories into reverse. Faraday drew diagrams based on his experiments, showing lines of electrical force that ignored conventional conductors and insulators. Clerk Maxwell's interpretation of Faraday's work showed waves traveling through space in what he supposed was the mysterious substance "ether."

Across that threshold, of course, lay the world we know: the world of radio waves, of electronics, of atomic subdivision, of radiation, of relativity. The inventions resulting from the scientific research of persons just across the threshold from Maxwell—J. J. Thomson, Roentgen, the Curies, Planck, Michelson, Morley, Einstein, and others—are the commonplaces of our lives. We have our teeth X-rayed, see the time in the dark from the radium on our watches, listen to the radio or watch television, shudder at the threat of the A-bomb, are surrounded by a hundred other push-button devices that were undreamed of when Michael Pupin stood in Cambridge on the other side of the threshold from our world. Yet the dawn was already gray: Pupin could almost see the forms the "poems of science" would take.

That was what made him restless; he was aware of the revolution. What, he kept asking himself, is light? It was a question few had asked in most of the nineteenth century. But Clerk Maxwell had asked it, and Maxwell's question haunted Pupin. The worst of it was that Maxwell had answered his own question and Pupin could not understand the answer. Neither, apparently, could anyone at Cambridge.

To try to find out, Pupin went to what he thought was a lonely place in Maxwell's Scotland to study Maxwell's theory. The place turned out to be not so lonely, and the Scotch lads and lassies who were there on vacation interrupted him. It gives a glimpse of Pupin's flexible temperament to learn that, instead of grinding on Maxwell, he spent his time learning to dance the Highland fling. Actually, he was dead tired from overwork, and he gladly surrendered himself to this frivolity. There was nothing "long-haired" about Michael Pupin.

At the end of vacation he knew he was through with Cambridge. It could teach him nothing more unless it gave him a laboratory. So he left for Berlin, where he knew he could work with experimental physicists.

Berlin was difficult for Pupin to face because of his early hatred of everything Teutonic. His boyhood bitterness toward the Austrian "tyrants" who had oppressed his native land extended to Germany as well, for Germans—in his youthful view—shared the "brutishness" of the Austrian masters. But after he had arrived in the dreaded city, the Germans he worked with showed him such kindness that he soon came to revise his beliefs.

Germany in the eighties was at the peak of her greatness. Bismarck had established the German Empire, uniting its diverse and mutually hostile states, and was showing himself to be a wise, if not a benevolent, ruler. German universities were drawing earnest and brilliant students from every part of the world. German scientists were more numerous than those of any other nation, and in certain fields, such as chemistry and metallurgy, they were supreme. Also, in Germany, the alliance between basic research and industry was extremely close; her great career in steel, for instance, was beginning as a result of intensive experimentation in the chemistry of iron. At the time of Pupin's stay there the tragic trend responsible for two world wars had not yet commenced.

Pupin's German teacher was the celebrated Hermann von Helmholtz, then in his sixties. Helmholtz might be called the middle link in the chain that led to the inventions of radio communication: Henry and Faraday—Maxwell — Helmholtz — J. J. Thomson — Crookes — Lodge. Without that chain of "pure" scientists, Marconi, Fleming, De Forest, and all the other inventors would not have known where to begin.

Pupin arrived in Berlin still haunted by the question, "What is light?" He was surprised when Helmholtz explained Maxwell's theory so simply that it was instantly clear. So, he thought, one must go to Germany to get clarification of an English discovery! Maxwell had found that light traveled through space in waves that were exactly like electromagnetic waves except for a difference like that of the bass and treble notes of a musical instrument in rapidity of vibrations. Light, then, may be said to be the result of an electromagnetic disturbance precisely like the waves that, today, we call radio waves.

This was Clerk Maxwell's theory; he stated it in more or less these words, and he used mathematical equations to show those who understood such things that the theory was true. But he did not prove it experimentally, so that its truth remained unclear even to many of his colleagues. But while Pupin was in Berlin, a Helmholtz pupil, Heinrich Hertz, set up apparatus and with it performed experiments that convinced everyone who saw them. His simple gadgets included an "oscillator" consisting of two spheres with a short gap between them and a ring "detector" at a distance. When the oscillator was charged by an electrical machine, sparks jumped across the gap, and when they jumped, a current moved in the detector. This was precisely the experiment Joseph Henry had performed on the Princeton campus some forty years before, but now, thanks to Maxwell, Hertz could tell *why* these results were obtained. They came about when the electromagnetic waves moving out from the spark gap struck the detector. Hertz went on to measure wave lengths and frequencies, and he also showed how the waves were reflected and refracted from insulators just as light waves were by mirrors and prisms.

Pupin lived long enough to see certain aspects of Maxwell's theories modified—such as Maxwell's belief in "ether" as a rarefied substance in space—but he also lived to see the practical uses of wireless telegraphy and radio broadcasting, which came when inventors followed the scientists. But in Berlin he was satisfied when that troublesome question about light was answered, and he went on to other things—among them the rapidly advancing science of "physical chemistry" that the great American, Willard Gibbs, had brought into the limelight at Yale.

Something else, too, came into his life at this time. When his mother died in Idvor, the memory of all the sound advice she had given him, which permeated every department of his life, came clear and sharp before him. One bit, concerning his future, was in the oft-repeated caution: "When you marry, Misha, marry an *American* girl." In Berlin he had been drawn to a German *mädchen,* just as in Scotland, a lassie, teaching him the Highland fling, had attracted him. Then an accident or coincidence suddenly crystallized his mother's wish. The sister of an American fellow student in Berlin came to visit him and as soon as Pupin saw her, he felt as if his mother's advice might come true. As the girl traveled from Berlin on a tour, he forgot Maxwell and Helmholtz and Hertz and light and electromagnetism and followed her all over Europe. They were married just as a call came from New York; the call that made Michael Pupin a scientist behind the inventors.

Fifteen years after he had arrived in New York as a penniless immigrant, a "greenhorn" in the land of opportunity, he entered the new Columbia School of Mines as a "Teacher of Mathematical Physics in the Department of Electrical Engineering."

It was something of a shock to him after his European experience to find how scantily equipped his alma mater still remained for scientific work. The new department was housed in a small brick shed called by the students the "cowshed." Pupin remembered that "the laboratory equipment consisted of a dynamo, a motor, and an alternator, with some so-called practical measuring instruments." Also, among the engineering students there was little understanding of an electrical "science." The chemists thought electrical engineering was primarily chemical because of the galvanic batteries and some new electrochemical processes, while the mechanical engineers thought it belonged to them because of dynamo and motor construction. But, from the beginning it had been the fate of America's top-ranking men of science to work in a climate of relative ignorance: Franklin, Henry, Willard Gibbs, and Pupin's friends, Henry Rowland and Elihu Thomson, among them. In spite of the difficulties, or perhaps because of them, these men rose to a greatness that matched that of their European contemporaries. Pupin, surely, was not disheartened by the obstacles he met.

It was a great age in America. Even against a scanty native background of science, the United States was rapidly advancing toward its place of industrial leadership of the world. Inventors such as Edison and engineers such as Nikola Tesla, George Westinghouse, and Charles Steinmetz were putting the mysterious electrical force to practical uses on a vast scale. That such geniuses may have borrowed much of their scientific theory from abroad does not diminish their achievements.

In the nineties, the power of Niagara Falls was hitched to giant generators. Distances over which electric power could be transmitted were enormously increased. Alternating current, once held in contempt, was coming into its own. The Tesla polyphase motor, which in '88 had only the capacity to drive a ten-inch ventilating fan, developed thousands of horsepower in the nineties. In this same decade, the General Electric Company was founded.

Yet the thing that most captured Pupin's fancy in the middle years of that decade came from abroad. When the news of Roentgen's X-rays came from Germany in 1895, Pupin forgot everything else. In the following year, he obtained the first X-ray photograph in America. His success with photographs taken with the aid of Edison's fluorescent screen made him instantly famous among doctors. He was so besieged by reporters that

> I had to lock myself up in my laboratory . . . in order to protect myself from continuous interruptions. The physicians brought all kinds of cripples for the purpose of having their bones photographed. . . . The famous surgeon, the late Doctor Bull of New York, sent me a patient with nearly a hundred small shot in his left hand. . . . He was in agony . . .[32]

After a few unsuccessful attempts,

> A beautiful photograph was obtained with an exposure of a few seconds. The photographic plate showed the numerous shot as if they had been drawn with pen and ink. Doctor Bull operated and extracted every one of them . . .[33]

But Pupin's work with the new rays proved too much for him. In a condition of weakness due to overwork, he nearly died from an attack of pneumonia. When he recovered, he found that his wife had died from the same disease, and the shock threw him into a breakdown that incapacitated him for more than a year. What restored him was a sudden interest in the training of horses and dogs. When, at last, he was able to go back to work, he went, not as a student of scientific theory, but as the inventor for which he acquired his greatest celebrity.

Actually, he had begun work on his invention in 1894 before the X-rays distracted him. After his breakdown, he turned back to his earlier experiments. And this renewed interest had the psychological value of bringing back memories of his earliest boyhood.

From his cattle-watching in the Banat pastures, he knew that sound travels through the ground better and farther than through the air. The solider the medium and the more resistant, the better the waves travel. Later he had found that vibrations move better over a string to which weights are attached at intervals than over an unweighted string. As Pupin expressed it:

> A light silk cord stretched between two fixed points and carrying at equidistant points heavy bird-shot will act like a uniform cord for all vibratory motions the wave-length of which embraces several intervals separating the bird-shot, and will transmit these motions much more efficiently from one end of the cord to the other than if the bird-shot were not there.[34]

The weights produced a better medium for the transmission of the vibratory waves, just as the more resistant water or earth made a better medium for the sound waves. Now, thought Pupin, as all waves had been shown to be alike except for frequency, could not the principle be applied electrically?

Telephone people in the nineties had been exasperated by the fact that while speech could be easily transmitted over short distances, the sound faded out when the distance was increased. Was there not some way in which an electric wire carrying a current could be weighted just as the silk cord was? "No," said the telephone experts, "we have tried that. We have put inductance coils at intervals along our wire so as to produce 'boosters' as the bird-shot had done." Pupin was not in the least thrown off by these failures. He tried the same coils and

> I succeeded because I did not guess: I was guided by the mathematical solution of the generalized La Grangian problem. What does this solution say when applied to electrical motions in a wire? It says this: Place your inductance coils into your telephone line at such distances apart that for all vibratory motions of electricity which it is desirable to transmit there shall be several coils per wave length. In telephonic transmission of speech that means one coil every four or five miles on overhead wires, and one coil in about one or two miles in a telephone cable.[35]

In other words, Pupin brought his studies in theoretical science to bear on the practical problem. He was, in short, one of the scientists behind his own invention.

He did not tell what the American Telephone and Telegraph Company paid him for the device that first made long-distance voice communication possible. He only said, "It gave me what I asked." Guesses have ranged from half a million to a million dollars, but, as Pupin himself tells us, Americans love legends.

Almost overnight, Michael Pupin's invention became famous throughout the civilized world. In France the telephone lines became *"pupinizé"*; in Germany *"pupinizierte linien"* sprang into being.

Is there a story that better links in one man European science and American invention? Across the Atlantic this immigrant boy built a bridge that has been traveled ever since and that finally brought science itself to our shores, where it might stand behind all future American invention.

SEVEN

The New Alchemy

A man and woman walked home through the dusk of an early Paris evening. They walked slowly, for they were tired. All day and for months of days they had worked together in a damp, rotting shed that they called their laboratory. For much of this time the woman had stood stirring a boiling mixture in an enormous pot with an iron rod that was almost as long as she was tall. Her husband had worked against heavy odds to measure the end products of the boiling with extremely delicate devices and instruments, whose functioning was affected by the dampness and the cold. The roof of the shed leaked, and there was not enough money anywhere to get it fixed. When the rain came, streams of water fell between these two workers and their work.

But now the stirring was over, and the hardest jobs of crystallizing and separating out the tiny quantities of precious substances that would carry proof to sceptical scientists everywhere were finally ended. At last these two had fulfilled a prophecy made four years before. So, in spite of their fatigue, their minds were on fire with the excitement of their triumph, and the time of their walking passed quickly.

In their flat, the wife went immediately to their four-year-old daughter, whom the nurse was preparing for bed. Taking the little girl from the nurse, the mother said, "I will bathe Irène. She likes me to put her to bed."

Her husband made a gesture of impatience.

"You think of nothing but that child."

"Nonsense, Pierre. I haven't thought of her once all day."

In her bed, the child's breathing gradually became regular, and, knowing that she slept, the mother went to join her husband. This little performance was a part of every evening, no matter how deep in their study these people might be. During the day it was necessary to leave Irène with a nurse, but no nurse was ever allowed to perform the intimate bedtime duties that were so important for the child's sense of security. Irène's mother may have been the greatest woman scientist that ever lived, but she was a mother too and a devoted one.

In the living room Pierre was pacing up and down. He always walked this way when he was thinking deeply. His wife sat down and took up some sewing. But she could not concentrate on it. Perhaps it was Pierre's pacing that distracted her. Perhaps it was her own urgent thought that made her get up after a time, throw down her work, and go to Pierre in breathless excitement.

"Irène's asleep," she said. "Let's go back there. I want to see It at night."

They always spoke of It, when they pronounced the word, as though it had a capital letter. They went back faster than they had come. Pierre unlocked the creaking door and opened it. The room was less dark than it had been on other nights. Here and there on shelves and tables there were tiny luminous spots—vaguely luminous, like glowworms or some phosphorescent creatures of the Gulf Stream.

"At last, Marie. We've waited a long time."

"But It's not as beautiful, Pierre, as you thought It would be. You thought of some vivid color."

"It is beautiful," Pierre said.

It was beautiful because it seemed to be part of themselves—as surely a fruit of their love as the child at home.

So they stood, that night, Pierre and Marie Curie on the threshold of a new world.

Marie Sklodovska was born in Warsaw in the winter of 1867. Her family was of that class of small landowners that has produced most of Poland's intellectuals: artists, writers, musicians, and scholars. Marie's father was a professor of physics and mathematics; her mother had conducted a girl's school, but this she gave up when her family grew so large that the double work was too much for her frail health. As no Polish child is ever called by her right name if a nickname can possibly be conjured up, Marie spent her girlhood as "Manya."

Poland, that perennially unhappy land, was under terrible pressures at this period. It was partitioned among Russia, Austria, and Prussia. Russia held the largest part and attempted with the utmost brutality to wipe out its Polish character. Even the Polish language was prohibited in the schools. Criticism of the Russian regime—and Russian Poland was a police state as regimented as Nazi Germany—meant deportation to Siberia. Polish patriotism, Polish colors, Polish national history, literature, and music were rigidly suppressed. There was, of course, an underground movement of rebellion, but this had to be buried in secrecy.

Manya, even as a young child, was passionately patriotic. She joined with other girls and boys in the exaltation of the national character, in organized hatred of Russia and every possible resistance to Czarist pressure. At the same time the teachers in her school made use of her cleverness to protect the school against Russian attack. She learned to speak Russian almost without an accent. Although all the students were required to study Russian history, Manya with her infallible memory learned the sequences of events and rulers so thoroughly that she could answer any question. Thus, whenever an inspector was sent by the Russian authorities to make sure the school was toeing the mark, little Manya was always called on to recite.

Manya Sklodovska was a completely normal child. She differed from her sisters and brothers and her classmates at school only in the power of her intellect. Her emotions were deep, her devotions passionate, and her will strong to the point of stubbornness. She adored her family, was willing to make any sacrifice for a brother or sister, and suffered agonies of homesickness when she was away from the family hearth. Yet she was not morbid or perverse, rarely angry, seldom introspective, and never self-centered. In spite of the considerable importance that her quick intelligence and high scholarship gained for her, she was without a trace of egotism or conceit. She was exuberant in pleasure and enjoyed every moment of recreation that, in a restricted and poverty-ridden life, was possible for her.

Always, she was a hard and tireless worker. She delved deep into mathematics. Nature was as exciting to her in its laws as in its moods of beauty. Anything to do with physics or chemistry wholly engrossed her. In a glass case in the parlor at home was a small collection of her father's laboratory instruments: delicate balances, an electroscope, test tubes, and mineral specimens. Before this, Manya would stand entranced for long moments, until the images burned themselves into her mind and the case became a life symbol. The memory of it remained with her always as a sort of reference point.

There was little relief for the uninterrupted work and daily drudgery of this family of small means. To Manya it was agony to watch the sinking health of her mother. Madame Sklodovska adored her children, but she could never kiss or caress them. She ate apart, her food was always on her special china that no one else must use, for she was incurably tubercular; she had a thorough understanding of her condition and a terror lest her children become infected. Her death inflicted on Manya a wound that was many years in healing.

Manya finished school at fifteen. Then came an interval of pure release. It was as though Fate had designed this compensation for a woman who would never again know rest. Her father had arranged for her to take a year's vacation, living with relatives in the country. She would pay her way with occasional tutoring of her child cousins or with very small payments of board. But in the main, she would be completely carefree. And, as her biographer writes:

> In the course of the mysterious passage called adolescence, while her body was transformed and her face grew finer, Manya suddenly became lazy. Abandoning the schoolbooks, she tasted, for the first and last time in her life, the intoxication of idleness.[36]

She became an expert rider and horsewoman; she played every sort of game with boys and girls of her age; in winter, she would skate and coast, go on long sleighrides, and dance through the night. One of her favorite pleasures was the "kulig," a rural Polish masquerade festivity.

> The "kulig" was . . . a dizzying, magic journey in the full excitement of carnival. Two sleighs went off in the evening over the snow with Manya Sklodovska and her three cousins, masked and dressed as Cracow peasant girls, huddled under the covers. Young men in picturesque rustic dress escorted them on horseback, brandishing torches. Other torches twinkled through the fir trees, and the cold night was filled with rhythm; the musicians' sleigh came up, bringing four . . . mad and charming creatures who for the next two nights and days would wring from their

fiddles the intoxicating tunes of the waltz, the krakoviak and the mazurka . . .[37]

Drawn by the music, sleighs from all over the country-side would then gather round the musicians and drive to the first house on the schedule. There the young people would dance, eat, and drink and go on to the next stop and so on until, a day and a night later, they would come to the last and biggest house for a long masque ball.

It was an unforgettable experience, and Marie remembered it all her life, as she would remember all the gay sweetness of that year. Because this memory was a comfort to this woman in the moments of her hardest trials, it must be an integral part of any story of her work.

When the idyllic year was over, the girl, mature now beyond her years and quite beautiful, returned with dynamic vigor to the work that led into her career. There was a considerable group of passionate students in Warsaw: young men and women willing to make any sacrifice toward their education. They formed together what they called the "Floating University," an organization for study independent of the Russian-controlled educational program. They met at one another's houses, and to Marie's great delight were able to get the use of a laboratory for scientific experimental work.

The students in the group were headed for various professions. Some, like Marie's brother Joseph and her sister Bronya, would become physicians. The majority would become teachers or professors, but they would go to posts outside captive Poland, where they would find freedom of expression. For Bronya and Marie the ideal and the hope was Paris. To be able to study at the Sorbonne or one of the great scientific schools of the University was, to the girls, the highest ambition they could imagine. But how, with the meager money that was available, could they even make the journey into France, not to speak of supporting themselves when they got there? Endlessly, the sisters talked and speculated and schemed; they saved and took what little jobs offered in the hope of accumulating some sort of a fund that they might jointly use. Meanwhile, both were hesitant about leaving their widowed father for whom they had kept house.

Marie Sklodovska insisted that Bronya be the first to go to Paris to study medicine while she would combine with her father (who was still teaching) to send what small sums of money they could. Marie was so stubborn that she finally broke her sister down. Bronya went, achieved a brilliant record at the university school of medicine, and, after a time, married a Polish medical student there. So she was able in the end to offer Marie some return for her aid.

Meanwhile, however, Marie had to find a way to earn a living. A post as governess away from Warsaw was offered her. To accept it, she would have to give up her studies and overcome her reluctance to leave her father. But this time he insisted, and it was soon evident to Marie that no other course was possible if Bronya was to be kept in Paris according to their promises.

The middle-class family to whom she went liked and admired her, but they made extreme demands. Besides teaching the spoiled and difficult children, she was made to play chess with the old people or to take part in the family's endless social activities. These things kept her from the private study she craved, and she was obliged to do her reading and solve her mathematical problems in the late hours when the others were in bed. But then sleep was always one of the least necessities in the life of Maria Sklodovska Curie.

There was one relieving circumstance that ended, however, in what for her was bitter tragedy. The older son of the family, a charming, gay, and handsome youth, was strongly attracted to her, and for the first time in her life she fell in love. He asked her to marry him, and she believed that they were engaged. But when the family were told, they became so enraged that the young people were forced to abandon their hope.

It is difficult for Americans to understand the European middle-class attitude toward marriage—especially in the last decade of the nineteenth century. To this wealthy Polish family who thought working for money was degrading, the idea of their handsome son—a likely catch for an heiress—marrying a penniless governess was unthinkable. And such was the power of parents, even over their adult sons, that the young man had no choice but to forget his love. To little Manya in this first awakening, the blow was hard to take, especially as her sense of truth was so far above the narrow social conventions. Yet later she must have blessed the fate that once again stepped in to direct her destiny.

After two years of this work as governess—in two families—Bronya invited her to live with her and her husband in Paris. For a while she refused—the burden would be too great. But at last, having saved enough to pay, along with her father's little contribution, for the journey and for her tuition, she rode on the hard wooden seats of a fourth-class railway carriage across Germany and into free France. In Paris, then, there began the most terrible and at the same time the most valuable years of her young life.

The exaltation that this poor Polish girl, not yet twenty-four, felt on her first ride atop a horse-drawn omnibus in Paris has been happily described by her daughter-biographer, Eve Curie.

At the moment when Manya, dulled by the tiresome journey, descended from the train to the smoky platform of the Gare du Nord, the familiar grip of servitude was suddenly loosened, her shoulders straightened, her lungs and heart felt at ease. For the first time she was breathing the air of a free country, and in her enthusiasm everything seemed miraculous. Miraculous that the passers-by who loitered along the pavement spoke the language they wanted to speak, miraculous that the booksellers sold works from the whole world without restraint. . . . Before and above everything else, it was miraculous that these straight avenues . . . were leading her, Manya Sklodovska, to the wide-open doors of a university. And what a university! The most famous. . . . The adventure was fit for a fairy tale. The slow, icy, disorderly omnibus was the enchanted carriage which took the poor fair princess from her modest lodging to the palace of her dreams.[38]

From the instant she arrived she became wholly, uniquely dedicated to work. She was soon discontented at her sister's apartment. She was at the Sorbonne all day but was obliged to spend the evening with her sister and her gay, amusement-loving brother-in-law. This kept her from her homework! She wanted to study till midnight. The others wanted to go to concerts. Or, both being physicians, they held consultations with their patients in the apartment. Marie could not bear the interruptions. So she left these people to whom she was devoted and got herself a tiny room close to the Sorbonne.

She gave up all recreation. She avoided friendships except with a few Polish students who were as eager for learning as she. She rejected the advances of the young men who were attracted by her blond beauty. Never again, she swore, would she let a man enter her life.

As time went on, her poverty increased. She moved from the modest room where she had been in some comfort to new bare quarters.

The room [Marie wrote in a reminiscence] . . . was in a garret, very cold in winter, for it was insufficiently heated by a small stove which often lacked coal. During a particularly rigorous winter, it was not unusual for the water to freeze in the basin in the night; to be able to sleep I was obliged to pile all my clothes on the bedcovers. In the same room I prepared my meals with the aid of an alcohol lamp and a few kitchen utensils. These meals were often reduced to bread with a cup of chocolate, eggs or fruit. I had no help in housekeeping and I myself carried the little coal I used up the six flights.[39]

How fortunate that she had had that year in the country: that year of riding, skating, dancing, and winter sports to build a body strong enough to endure these hardships! For a long time, she suffered no ill effects. Then one day she fainted from hunger. A friend took her to her sister: Bronya and her husband found her to be dangerously anemic; they kept her with them until, temporarily at least, her health was restored.

Meanwhile, her work was brilliant. When she was twenty-six she took her master's degree in physics, rating number one among those who passed the examination. The following year she was second in the master's examination in mathematics. Incidentally, she perfected herself in the French language to the point of almost wholly eliminating her accent. But she was happiest of all in the laboratory working with test tubes, retorts, and delicate precision instruments that brought alive in her mind her father's glass case in the Warsaw house—that shrine before which as a child she had stood in such worshipful awe. This was the kind of release that made the suffering possible.

So, in two years the fairy tale had become a pretty grim story for this Cinderella. But then, one day, suddenly, along came the prince.

. . .

A common friend of Marie Sklodovska and Pierre Curie invited them both, one night, to dinner. This Polish professor, Joseph Kovalski, had no thought of romance in bringing them together. Marie had asked him for advice about some work she was doing, and he had suggested that she ask a young man who was doing research in crystallography. "Come to dinner," he had added, "and I'll introduce you."

Pierre Curie was instantly impressed. It was unique in his experience to meet a woman to whom he could talk easily about science. But here was a girl, some seven years younger than he, to whom none of the terms he used was unfamiliar, who followed with instant sympathy his description of his experiments, and whose eyes lit with excitement at the possibilities in his research. And in addition to her easy understanding, she had grace and beauty. When they parted that night, he knew that he must see her again and again.

As they met, after that, now at a meeting of the Physics Society, then a few times in her garret, he became aware that her utter dedication to science was precisely his own. Finally he knew that if they both loved science so intensely, they must come to love each other. Each must be to the other a symbol of their common dedication. He told her this, but she said no; she had other attachments: to her family, to Poland for which she was homesick; she must go to see her old father; she was not ready for love. She was fighting, of course, for time in which to dissolve her oath against men and to reconcile the concepts of work and marriage. She went home to Poland the summer after she met him, and Pierre pursued her with some of the most beautiful love letters in the annals of science.

In the quiet of home life with the renewal of old associations, with new health from wholesome food and the rest she so desperately needed, the destiny ahead of her became clear in her mind. Yet even after she had come back to Paris in October, her chronic stubbornness kept her from spoken agreement until the spring. They were married in July, 1895, and rode away into the mountains and forests of France for their brief honeymoon on bicycles Marie had bought with money given her for her trousseau.

In that year of 1895, the German, William Roentgen, produced a new kind of ray resulting from the impact of a cathode ray against the glass of a vacuum tube. The ray, which bounced, he called X, on the principle that X is the name for anything that is unknown. The X-rays could penetrate opaque matter and, in the hands of inventors, became, as we know, one of the greatest aids to surgery ever devised. Roentgen's discovery spread throughout the scientific world an epidemic of inquiry into these emanations that resembled light yet were not visible in the spectrum. At the same time, they made an impression on a photographic plate.

Caught in this epidemic was a Frenchman, Henri

Becquerel. He found that there were emanations from the salts of the element uranium and that these rays could also penetrate opaque substances. He wrapped a photographic plate in black paper, put it in a dark room, placed a bit of uranium salt on it, and when he developed the plate, found an impression. So, he thought, uranium is fluorescent: that is, it absorbs light when it is exposed to light and gives it off later. But then he tried putting a bit of uranium salt that had *not* been exposed to light on the wrapped plate, and, sure enough, there was the impression again. Could it be possible, he wondered, that this substance gave off spontaneous rays? Without an electrical impulse as in the case of the cathode rays, source of the X-rays, and without exposure to light, these rays shot off continuously from the uranium salt. What was the answer? Was the element disintegrating, shooting particles of itself into space?

While he was wondering about this, Madame Curie got wind of his experiments and was fascinated by them. If uranium behaved in this way, might not other elements also send out rays? Patiently, she experimented with every known element. Aluminum, barium, bismuth, copper—down the list she went. Finally she found one—thorium—that answered the question. She announced this discovery and added, "I call these elements radio-active." In that moment she added a new immensely valuable word to the language. Today, we have eliminated the hyphen and write of "radioactivity."

As trained physicists always do when they make a discovery, Marie Curie made measurements. With a set of instruments arranged by her and Pierre, she determined the intensity of the rays by measuring the conductivity of the air surrounding the radioactive elements. She then became puzzled. Pitchblende, the ore that contained the uranium and the thorium, gave off rays more intense than either those of the thorium or the uranium. There must be then, she guessed, some other element or elements more intensely radioactive than either! Was she, she asked Pierre, about to unearth a hitherto unknown element? Pierre Curie who, like Pasteur, had gone a long distance into the investigation of crystallography was so fascinated by his wife's inquiry that he gave up everything else to help her.

Actually, after long experiment she found two highly radioactive elements in the pitchblende. One she called polonium after her beloved fatherland. The other she called radium.

By this time, a first child had been born to Pierre and Marie. They named her Irène. From now on, in spite of the intensely absorbing laboratory work, Marie Curie would divide her time between Irène and the mysterious pitchblende. Dramatic evidence of this is in the diary she kept in 1898 and '99. On October 17, 1898, she wrote in this book: "Irène can walk very well, and no longer goes on all fours." On January 5, 1899, she noted, "Irène has fifteen teeth." Between these comments was a note intended for the Academy of Science. This concluded with the words:

The various reasons we have just enumerated lead us to believe that the new radioactive substance [pitchblende] contains a new element to which we propose to give the name RADIUM . . .[40]

The note of which this was a sentence was duly published in the *Proceedings* of the Academy. Physicists and chemists everywhere read it and shook their heads. Who were these Curies? Sure enough, their records were good. They held masters' degrees. But their statement was a mere conjecture, a surmise. (Doubt, of course, is part of the equipment of a scientist.) Let them show us some pure radium! They say it is there in the pitchblende. But they have not extracted it, isolated it. Where is their proof?

So Marie, between her moments of delight at Irène's teeth and steps and words, her bathing and diet, and the bedtime stories, went back with Pierre to their laboratory and worked for four years to prove their statement.

In all Paris, that center of European scientific knowledge, there was not enough faith in the word of these two to provide them with a decent workshop. The School of Physics and Chemistry in the Rue Lhomond gave them what it could spare—an old wooden shed in a courtyard. Here the collaboration of husband and wife was so close that it is impossible to give special credits to one or the other. We only know that the initial impulse was Marie's.

The Curies were not disturbed by the sceptical reaction to their prophecy. They were familiar with the doubts that had proved so valuable in the history of science. Their own attitude was as sceptical toward the hypotheses of others as that which was now directed toward them. In this case they knew beyond question that they were right, but they did not blame the others. And they, too, wanted to have proof to show the world. Their only concern was that the material obstacles in the way seemed to require a superhuman effort.

In the first place, it was evident that the new elements existed in the pitchblende ore in only the tiniest traces. Although the radioactivity from radium, for instance, was, as the Curies announced "enormous," yet the amount of the radium producing this effect was imperceptible in the amounts of pitchblende at their disposal. Marie's first guess was 1 per cent. This turned out to be a million times too large! The amount they found was .0000001 per cent!

The problem then was to get enough pitchblende. Pitchblende was costly. Marie found, however, that once the uranium had been extracted from the ore, the residue—still containing the radium and polonium, which so few believed in—was considered worthless. Through a friend, the Curies found a mine in Austria where large quantities of this "useless" residue had accumulated. And this same friend persuaded the Austrian government to present a ton of the stuff to "the two French lunatics who thought they needed it."

It came at last, brought by a large horse truck. The sacks containing the ore were unloaded and piled in the old shed workshop. From then on, the work never stopped. As Marie afterward remembered it and wrote in the biography of her husband:

> I came to treat as many as twenty kilograms of matter at a time, which had the effect of filling the shed with great jars full of precipitates and liquids. It was killing work to carry the receivers, to pour off the liquids and to stir, for hours at a stretch, the boiling matter in a smelting basin.[41]

And yet, she added:

> In spite of the difficulties of our working conditions, we felt very happy. Our days were spent at the laboratory. In our poor shed there reigned a great tranquillity. . . . We lived in our single preoccupation as if in a dream.[42]

Eve Curie writes of her father's impatience with the infinitesimal results of the work. The time came, she says, when he was ready to abandon the attempt to prepare pure radium. But here Marie's native stubbornness triumphed.

> In 1902, forty-five months after the day on which the Curies announced the probable existence of radium, Marie finally carried off the victory in the war of attrition: she succeeded in preparing a decigram of pure radium. . . .
>
> The incredulous chemists . . . could only bow before the facts, before the superhuman obstinacy of a woman.[43]

The next four years were exceedingly fruitful not only for the Curies but also for scientists all over the world to whom new vistas of exciting research had been opened up by the discovery. With pure radium available to work with, they could go on in experiment after experiment to demonstrate the new theories of the composition and structure of matter. One startling result was proof that the particles of one element could contain tiny particles of other elements; that radioactivity was actually a process of dividing the atoms that for more than two thousand years had been thought indivisible. In short, the ancient dreams of alchemists had come true. The Curies had not, to be sure, turned lead into gold, but they had found helium gas in the emanations from radium! It was true that, even before the turn of the century, there had been guesses in the direction of what Marie called the "cataclysm of atomic transformation," but proof had to await the coming of the actual, violently radioactive substance that could be used in the laboratory for the infallible proofs of this new alchemy and of the new theories of atomic structure.

Then it was found that radium spontaneously generated heat. One of the most remarkable properties of radioactive substances was that this continuous emission of particles did not perceptibly diminish the substances from which they radiated. It came to be shown that for a quantity of radium to be reduced by one half would require sixteen hundred years. Then it was shown that the particles which flew off were themselves radioactive.

The discovery of radium became, therefore, a link between the past and the future of science. It was radium that finally convinced even the most doubting chemists that the old theories about matter must be completely revolutionized. It was radium that made possible Albert Einstein's experiments with velocities, which, as we shall see, gave the final equations in his theories of relativity. And the work of the Curies, led by Marie, was an indispensable step in the march toward the realization of atomic energy.

The immediate contribution to invention—and this is what made the production of radium an industry —was in the application of radium to medicine. It was found that the emanations from radium had the power of destroying diseased cells in the body. Thus certain cancerous conditions could be cured. When the doctors —true inventors as we saw in the cases that followed Pasteur's discoveries—began to apply radium treatments, the wholesale manufacture of radium began. The work of the Curies in their wooden shed was magnified many times in factories, such as that of the Central Chemical Products Company in France and, later, in similar establishments in many parts of the world.

Four years after the triumph in the Rue Lhomond, the idyllic partnership was dissolved by a tragedy from which Marie could never wholly recover. She went on, after it, to new, magnificent work and to fame such as few women—and no woman scientist—have known. She received a second Nobel Prize following the one that came to her from her first discovery. She was given five other major prizes, sixteen medals, and nineteen honorary doctorates from colleges and universities—nine of them in America. She visited America, and Americans surrounded her, as her daughter saw, "with an almost religious devotion." Yet nothing compensated for her loss.

It was a spring day in Paris. Pierre was walking home deep, as usual, in thought. Always absent-minded he was more so than ever that afternoon. He was walking in the street behind a horse cab, which obscured his view ahead. The cab came to a corner; he turned away from it and walked head on into a team of huge horses that were pulling a heavy wagon. Between them Pierre fell, and though the driver tried to halt them, the heavy wheel of the cart had passed over his skull before they stopped.

When, an hour later, Marie came home knowing nothing of what had happened, she found a silent group of men: her old father, Pierre's father, and two professors. As they stood there facing her, waiting to tell the incredible news, she felt the air of foreboding in the room. But she waited. And then Paul Appell, the professor who from her earliest days in Paris had thrilled her with his lectures, spoke. He gave a simple, factual account of the accident.

"But Pierre is dead? Absolutely dead?"

Marie's words ended an idyll as beautiful as any in the history of marriage.

Marie Curie lived to see her story repeated. Irène of the "fifteen teeth" grew into a woman with the same interests as her mother's. For a long time she helped fill the gap left by her father's death by constant companionship with her mother. From both parents she inherited her massive intellect. From Marie she learned the deep secrets of radiology and chose science for her career. At twenty-nine, she married Frédéric Joliot, a brilliant worker at the Institute of Radium, which her parents had founded. Together, the Joliot-Curies carried on the research Irène's mother had begun and, a dozen years after their marriage, won the Nobel Prize for the discovery of artificial radioactivity. Marie died on the eve of the award.

There is no parallel in the personal records of science to the dynasty of the Curies. The combination of perfect professional collaboration with love, domestic harmony, and mutual affection has built a story that must stand as an inspiration to countless generations of young researchers. It was, too, a fairy tale beyond little Manya's most fanciful dreams.

EIGHT

$E = mc^2$

Through an enormous applauding, cheering crowd, held back by police to make a pathway for him, there passed a man with a brier pipe in one hand and a violin case in the other. To all appearances, he was a musician come to New York for a concert. He looked like a musician with his abundance of hair, his absent-minded manner as though he were imagining a symphony. But if an unknowing bystander, whose curiosity had been attracted by the crowd, had asked someone, "Who is that violinist they are all cheering?" he would have been told: "He is not a violinist—or rather, not a professional musician. He is a scientist—a great scientist."

"But what has he done to have so many admirers?"

And then the informant would have turned to someone else in the crowd to ask, "Yes, just what *has* he done?" And the question might have gone on through the thousands who had come to see this great man, and not one of them could have answered.

It was said that only twelve persons in the world really understood precisely what Albert Einstein meant in his theory of relativity. Yet in every civilized place all who read the newspapers or listened to their neighbors' talk knew that Einstein was a genius, that he had overthrown all the foundations on which physics and chemistry and astronomy had rested for two hundred years and upset all previous human concepts of the universe. And later they learned that this revolution had made possible the development of television, of the photoelectric cell, of a whole new sequence of electronic inventions, and, finally, of the release of atomic energy for power and for bombs.

Men and women, eager boys and girls whose education was moving into the realm of science, tried to explain relativity and the equivalence of mass and energy to each other with varying success. There was an epidemic of books full of "simple" diagrams and analogies. It was not difficult to see that a fly walking along the top of a moving train moved at one speed relative to the train and at another relative to the ground and at still another from the point of view of an observer in space who could consider the motions of the earth in addition to those of fly and train. And from these facts it was not hard to agree with Einstein's belief that there was no absolute motion and no absolute rest: that every motion in the universe was relative to some other motion. That the universes of Copernicus and Newton, which had determined useful calculations for hundreds of years, were thus thrown into the discard was also easy to see and that physicists must form other notions on which to base new calculations. Moreover, along with the revolution, an element of uncertainty had crept in, requiring a new opening of the minds that Newton and his disciples had so comfortably closed.

$$E = mc^2$$

But then, going on from there, the way became rougher. Experiments that threw the ether theory out the window, that added the fourth dimension of time, or that proved the constancy of the velocity of light took more study, as did those in which rays of light separated electrons from their atoms. Finally, we found ourselves in a realm in which the language we had been accustomed to speak and read disappeared and was replaced by unfamiliar signs and symbols, Greek letters, dashes and crosses. So, for a while, if we were going deeply into this thing, we must drop all effort to explain in words and become trained in the use of that tool without which modern physicists can do virtually nothing, for mathematics *is* for most practical scientists a tool: a means of interpreting natural laws when words fail. It is a kind of shorthand for verbal statement. It has the advantage of being universal; it needs no translation for the English, German, French, or Russian student. It is only in the highest regions of thought that mathematics becomes more than a tool. There, mathematicians have been said to come closer to God than some clergymen; there, they may evolve concepts that they sometimes believe are more beautiful and more moving than anything in art or poetry; there, too, in the apparent approach to infinity, they encounter the uncertainties that are bewildering to so many cosmic students today.

Our story must stop, of course, before it reaches the point where sentences turn into equations, and the best we can do is to try to tell what the hieroglyphics mean by simplified—a physicist would say oversimplified—analogies and comparisons.

A few brilliant writers who were masters of both languages—mathematics and English—have done this, and the world owes them a great debt, for no one in this twentieth century can afford not to have touched the fringe of Einstein's universe. Back in the 1920's that magnificent popular interpreter of science, Edwin Emery Slosson, first opened the door with *Easy Lessons in Einstein.* In late years the subject has been treated as simply but more fully in Lincoln Barnett's incomparable *The Universe and Dr. Einstein* and, in a more limited way, in J. G. Feinberg's *The Atom Story.* These books tell all we need to know—unless we are to become scientists ourselves—but also what we *must* know in order to be civilized citizens of a twentieth century world.

In the city of Ulm on the Danube the boy was born on the fourteenth of March, 1879. His father, a free-thinking Jew, owned and administered a small electrochemical factory; his mother, descended from a line of Swabian country folk, was far removed from the rigid, austere Germans who, under Bismarck, were coming to design the empire's future. The Swabians were gentle, fun-loving and artistic.

As Albert grew, it was evident that he was neither German nor Jew in spirit but destined for citizenship in a world of his own—a world without nationality and religious sect. He loathed with an almost pathological hatred the goose-stepping discipline that he saw round him and that was coming to be the German fashion. The sight of soldiers on parade turned him sick, and school, as it was taught in most of Germany, seemed to be run by sergeants. The notion that a boy should learn by rote something that he did not understand was instinctively repellent to him. As a result, he cut school when he could and wandered off into the fields to dream about the way things should be in a world divinely instead of humanly ordered.

Two things saved the boy from despair at one extreme and rabid rebellion at the other. One was the teaching, by an engineer uncle, of the elements of mathematics. The other was the violin. It was music that gave him his sense of the prevailing harmony in the universe and the craving to understand that harmony and ally himself with it. Playing his violin, he was transported out of the chaos—as it seemed to him—of human society. The music carried him into another world.

He was not yet ten when his Uncle Jake began to instruct him in algebra. "It is a merry science," the engineer would say. "When the animal we are hunting cannot be caught, we call it x temporarily and continue to hunt it until it is bagged." When Uncle Jake started him on equations, nothing could stop him. His first reading of geometry had an extraordinary effect—almost like that of the violin. "The world," writes his biographer,

Philipp Frank, "with its disorder and uncleanliness suddenly appeared to him to contain also an element of intellectual psychological order and beauty."

As the Einstein family had moved from Ulm to Munich during Albert's infancy, the boy got his first schooling there. It was in a Catholic school. He shuttled between Catholic doctrine in school and what Jewish beliefs were still held at home. He took a certain pleasure in both, yet all the time he was constructing in the back of his mind a religion that was independent of all professed faith. God, in his growing consciousness, was the God of the universe, personally inaccessible at least until one identified one's self with that universe.

Eventually, Albert went to a *gymnasium*—the German name for secondary school—and became more bored than ever because his learning had outgrown orthodox teaching. One day a teacher took him aside and said:

"Please, Albert, don't ask me those questions in public. It embarrasses me to have to say, in front of the other pupils, that I don't know the answers!"

In all these growing years, young Einstein tended to be a solitary. He was called antisocial. He made few friends. He was shy and feared contact with other boys lest it interrupt or distort his thinking. He was in constant friction with his teachers. He refused to accumulate facts in his memory. Why burden your brain, he said, with things you could look up when you needed them? Worst of all from the teachers' view, he was unpatriotic, as German patriotism was understood.

But these were only beginnings. The adult Einstein moved away from some of these pressures. Still, it is necessary to know a man's beginnings for the full understanding of his ends, for some residue of them always remains.

Home, during his boyhood, helped pull him out of the worst of his distresses. Its atmosphere of cheerful kindness and tolerance compensated for the hurts at school. The brutal anti-Semitism, for instance, of which he was the target, was relieved by the humor of his mother, so that it became ridiculous and unreal. Unhappily, however, this family comfort was short-lived. Hermann Einstein ran into financial trouble. His business fell away, and he became convinced that there was little hope of improvement while he stayed in Munich. Being, like the legendary Wandering Jew, without strong national ties, he went south to Italy and set up his factory in Milan. Albert, he thought, was old enough now to board at the house of a family friend in Munich and finish his education there.

The boy was rarely troubled by loneliness—indeed he often sought it—but to be alone in a hostile land was more than he could bear. Schoolmates and teachers alike were against him, so he persuaded the family physician to tell the director of the *gymnasium* that he was too ill to work. And if, with William James, one admits sickness of the soul as a disease, one must agree that the doctor told the truth. The director was only too glad to let Albert go —he formally expelled him from the school—and the boy made his way to Milan, where, in a joyous moment, he joined the family circle again.

Geniuses of Einstein's cast of mind usually educate themselves. They may soar so high over their fellows that school holds them back. The months Albert spent in Italy were a release from the German *gymnasium's* drag on his progress. To him, the interval was pure heaven. Now he could read what he wanted, explore where his curiosity led him. He could walk alone over the hills and think. He could play the eternal game of equations, inventing and solving the problems that drew him ever farther into outer space, into the concert of the spheres. At night, the stars in the Lombard sky seemed nearer than ever.

He read not only in physics or in the mathematical representations of physics in advanced algebra, analytic geometry, and calculus—all of which he had mastered by the time he was fourteen—but in that beginning of adolescence, he also digested the whole of Immanuel Kant's *Critique of Pure Reason,* a metaphysical work not understood by the average person.

This idyllic existence could not last. Again the family fortune declined, and Albert knew that his presence was a financial burden on his father. He knew he must earn his own living. As nothing could induce him to return to Munich, he made his way to Switzerland, determined to live from day to day by any jobs that offered, but equally determined to let nothing keep him from the higher education necessary for a professional career.

There were good schools in Zurich. He was too young for the University, which required certain diplomas for admission. He tried the Polytechnic School, which was world-famous. He astonished the professors with his grasp of mathematics. But he was deficient in history, geography, economics, and other subjects, so he took the advice of those familiar with the Swiss educational program and went to a preparatory school at Aarau.

He was reluctant to enter another secondary school. But he found Aarau wholly different from Munich. The unreasoning martinet discipline—"sergeant" discipline as he called it—was unknown. The sort of sincerity, tolerance, and humility he had associated with home was there in the school. Everyone was friendly. There was no racial antagonism; young Einstein was accepted on the common basis—a basis of earnest curiosity in the pursuit of learning. For the first time in his life he made friends among boys of his own age. In this serene and gentle social climate his bitter prejudices dropped away.

This prepared him for the life of the true scholar he was to live at the Zurich school and later at the University. At Zurich, the power of his intellect, his long reach toward a new cosmic philosophy, and the indomitable urgency of his searching mind won respect and admiration. Again he made friends; too many, perhaps, for his comfort, for they would talk all night.

All this time he was desperately poor, often hungry. Yet in any educational community there are always jobs, ill-paying as they may be. What with tutoring boys, assisting professors, and winning, by some brilliant paper, an occasional award, he was able to keep his body and his restless soul together until he could find some permanent outside work. He was able to live frugally because of the fewness of his needs. He had no desire for possessions. The least possible food and clothing were enough. Throughout his life, indeed, his only laboratory consisted of a pad of paper and a pencil or fountain pen.

He got a good job, finally, in the patent office at Berne. The work was easy, the hours convenient, and the pay good. The job did not interfere with his studies. Einstein's boss was relatively easy-going. His only insistence was that his employees should not have extracurricular interests while they were in the office. This irked Einstein because what he was expected to do took so little time and idleness was hateful to him, so he devised a way of playing his equation game all day. Whenever he heard the boss's step, he would thrust the scraps of paper on which he was working into a drawer kept open for the purpose.

Exhaustively, he read the works of every theoretical physicist in the long chain back to Newton and Galileo.

$$E = mc^2$$

Helmholtz, Kirchhoff, Boltzmann, Clerk Maxwell, and Hertz came in for especial scrutiny. All this time he became increasingly aware that none of these great men had quite arrived at the truths he sought. And all this time, he was sure that there were holes in the scheme of nature that was so universally accepted.

Scientists and philosophers are beginning to doubt that man can ever discover total reality. That is because lately invented instruments and processes suggest the existence of many things and forces that our senses cannot perceive. If all these exist in "reality," though imperceptibly, how many more may there not be beyond even the power of the most delicate instrument imaginable to detect?

There are cases in which the very effort to observe destroys the object of our observation. For example, there was Einstein's discovery of the photoelectric effect, which makes it impossible ever to see an electron, even if a microscope could be invented that would magnify it a hundred billion times. That is because of the violent effect of light or other rays upon electrons. The light that would make the electron visible to the eye, or the X-ray that could cause a photographic impression of it, knocks the tiny thing out of the field of vision of the human or camera eye. Yet we know the electron exists because of phenomena such as the deposit of carbon on the inside of a light bulb, which cannot otherwise be explained. Thus scientific experimenters have come to assume the existence of more and more things that cannot be seen, heard, felt, smelled, or tasted.

In the days of Newton, men had to base their cosmic theories or their discoveries of physical laws on the phenomena they could perceive with their senses. Isaac Newton, observing the effects of gravitation, electricity, and magnetism believed them to be different, distinct forces. But when the electromagnet arrived, two of these forces were seen to be the same. Light was something else again. A ray of light was split by Newton into a spectrum of colors running from red to violet, and that seemed all there was to it. The human eye could perceive nothing more. But the invention of photography showed that there was a great deal more. Photographs could be made by rays that were invisible to the eye as light. Beyond each end of the visible spectrum were found rays that were called ultraviolet and infrared. Could they too be called light rays, though they could not be seen? Then an experimenter named Hertz invented devices that proved Clerk Maxwell's hypothesis that light moved in the same kind of waves as those which carried electromagnetic disturbances, and after that scientists came to know that X-rays and radio waves and possibly others differed from light only in wave length. And when the Curies opened the door on radiation, the spectrum lengthened again. All this progress made the cleavage between seen and unseen, between apparent and real, sharper; and it was obvious that there was far too much in the invisible world for any compact little seventeenth or eighteenth century theory to explain.

Yet within those boundaries, the scheme evolved by Galileo, Newton, and their followers was so mechanically perfect and worked so well for most practical purposes that scientists were reluctant to abandon it. They even invented ingenious fictions to support it. Newton had believed that in space there was absolute rest; that space had physical being and that within it, while it remained stationary, the celestial bodies continued their motions. Though there was no scientific proof of this, the discoveries of the next two centuries convinced experimenters that it was so. As Lincoln Barnett tells us in *The Universe and Dr. Einstein:*

> with the development of the wave theory of light scientists found it necessary to endow empty space with certain mechanical properties—to assume, indeed, that space was some kind of substance. . . . And to eighteenth and nineteenth century physicists it was obvious that if light consisted of waves, there must be some medium to support them, just as water propagates the waves of the sea and air transmits the vibrations we call sound. Hence when experiments showed that light can travel in a vacuum, scientists evolved a hypothetical substance called "ether" which they decided must pervade all matter. . . . When Maxwell finally identified light as an electromagnetic disturbance the case for ether seemed assured.[44]

When a belief is accepted by so many wise and profound minds, it takes independence and courage to doubt it—in public at least. Even late in the nineteenth century, this "ether" was taken for granted by men of science, as were certain "axioms" of geometry such as the eternal separation of parallel lines or as John Locke and Thomas Jefferson took for granted the "self-evident truth" that all men are created equal.

Albert Einstein, however, took nothing for granted. He had read about all the theories and he had gone ahead with his independent thinking. He had become convinced that there was no such thing as absolute rest or absolute motion. Therefore, he could not accept the existence of the ether. At the same time he had no proof of its nonexistence. But while he was trying to invent some mathematical or physical method of proof, he came suddenly upon a piece of information that, with all his study, had escaped him.

Perhaps because they had worked in that scientifically backward nation, the United States, the extraordinary experiment made by two American professors in Cleveland in 1881 had not got into the exceedingly large body of scientific literature studied by Einstein. Perhaps because the proof demonstrated by Albert Abraham Michelson and Edward Williams Morley completely demolished the ether theory, it was not thought acceptable. But the chances are, as Mr. Barnett suggests, that scientists were so embarrassed by the doubts into which the Michelson-Morley experiment threw them that they could not form any new conclusion about the natural laws.

$$E = mc^2$$

It was a serious dilemma [Barnett tells us], and one that split scientific thought for a quarter century.[45]

The experiment was a simple one, though it required an exceedingly delicate instrument for measuring light velocity. With it one ray of light was sent in the direction of the earth's rotary motion so that the ether through which the earth turns should retard it. Another ray was sent at right angles to the first, in a direction in which the ether stream, if any, could not affect it. Again a ray was sent against the direction of the earth's rotation, hence *with* the ether stream. The velocity of the three was found to be precisely the same. The propagation of none of the rays was either retarded or accelerated. This left the scientists with two choices. Unless they forgot about the ether, they would have to assume that the earth was standing still. But if they abandoned the ether, what were they to put in its place?

As soon as he read of the American experiment, the fog through which Einstein had been groping suddenly cleared. Now that he was certain that there was no ether, the whole concept of space as a framework absolutely at rest fell away. His mind reached out to the remotest part of the universe, and he saw every particle of matter constantly in motion—not in motion as opposed to rest, but in motion that related to the motion of some other particle. As Barnett again states:

Einstein seized on this as a revelation of universal law. If the velocity of light is constant regardless of the earth's motion, he reasoned, it must be constant regardless of the motion of any sun, moon, star, meteor, or other system moving anywhere in the universe. From this he drew a broader generalization, and asserted that the laws of nature are the same for all uniformly moving systems. This simple statement is the essence of Einstein's Special Theory of Relativity.[46]

Einstein made this declaration when he was only twenty-six. According to one biographer—Gordon Garbedian—the young man, still working in the patent office at Berne, "was so overwhelmed by the vast implications of his discovery that he was ill for fourteen days."

In his first paper on relativity—*The Special Theory of Relativity*—Einstein went further than a mere denial of absolute rest and absolute motion. He denied the existence of space except as a possible order of material objects. We say, for instance, the earth is here, the sun is there, the moon is somewhere else, and between them there is "space"—really just a word to indicate that these bodies are separated, that there is distance between them. But the "space" itself is zero, emptiness. If you should remove earth, moon, and sun, there would be nothing. So space is not a thing like air or water any more than "distance" is a thing: you cannot handle distance or boil it or freeze it—there would be no such thing as distance unless there were points for it to be between. You can measure it only from points of reference.

Einstein then denied time except as a possible order of events. There is no absolute time apart from happenings any more than there is absolute space apart from the things in it. But such events as sunrise, sunset, and the seasons suggest to us that there is an interval between them just as there is distance between material objects. But just as there would be no distance or space without the objects, so, too, there would be no time without the events. Time as a measurement is, however, as essential to practical living as distance is; otherwise we would have no sense of order. So we have invented sundials and yard-sticks, clocks and speedometers. Actually, however, man lived the greatest part of his time on earth with no means of measuring time except solar, lunar, and stellar movements, which produced risings, settings, springs, summers, autumns, and winters—things he could see and feel. Poets and philosophers have occasionally believed that this must have been pleasant indeed without the tyranny of the clock that has made slaves of us all.

> The experiences of an individual [said Einstein] appear to us arranged in a series of events; in this series the single events which we remember appear to be ordered according to the criterion of "earlier" and "later." There exists, therefore, for the individual, an I-time, or subjective [personal] time. This itself is not measurable. I can, indeed, associate numbers with the events, in such a way that a greater number is associated with the later event than with an earlier one.[47]

Thus we can tag the sunrise with the number seven and call the sun's position in the zenith twelve and thereby assure ourselves that noon is later than dawn, but if we were shut in a dark room without a timepiece, we should have no chance to tag these things and so should have no sense of earlier or later, before or after, except, perhaps, the voice of our bodily needs.

But Einstein, years afterward, when he had become famous, put the question of absolute time more crudely and humorously. His secretary, whose duty it was to handle his enormous fan mail, came to him one day in despair. "All these people," she said "want to know what 'relativity' is. What can I tell them?"

"Well," he replied, "if a man sits for an hour with a pretty girl it will seem like a minute but if he sits for a minute on a hot stove, it will seem like an hour. That's Relativity!"

The more Einstein contemplated space and time—to Newton, separate entities and existing independently of the human mind—the more they seemed to be parts, so to speak, of the same picture puzzle. And this was the great aim of Einstein's exploration of Nature: to reduce all the physical phenomena to different aspects of the same phenomenon; in other words, to reduce the number of separate things we should have to worry about in the universe. It pleased him to find, for instance, that electricity, magnetism, and light were the same except for frequency of vibration. Now it pleased him to think that time and space were dependent one upon the other. After his assumption that everything in the universe was constantly in motion, he began to think of time as a dimension. This must be so if nothing is at rest. The familiar three spatial dimensions—length, breadth, and thickness—applied to a body at rest. But when that body is in motion—perhaps very rapidly in motion—must not some other measurement be applied?

When we measure the distance to a star, time enters into our measurement. We say a certain star or galaxy is fifty or a hundred or thousands of "light years" away, meaning that light, traveling at the velocity of approximately 186,000 miles a second, takes that many years to reach us. We see the star, therefore, not as it is now but as it was fifty, a hundred, or thousands of years ago. Today it may have ceased to exist! So time becomes a factor in our calculation of distance.

Time as a dimension figured in what Einstein called a "space-time continuum." A railroad track running from New York to Chicago is a two-dimensional space-time continuum. But when a train travels over the track, a third dimension is added to your mental picture. You cannot describe the train except in terms of the time it takes to get from one point to another. Any other image of a train is meaningless. Similarly, the route of an airplane is a three-dimensional continuum; add time and you have four dimensions. In short, all objects in motion have this added dimension, and Einstein says all objects are in motion relative to something else.

A more difficult concept is that of the changes in the size of a moving body as its velocity increases. At velocities approaching that of light, a measuring rod becomes shorter, that is, it contracts in the direction of motion. If it could reach the speed of light, it would cease to exist. Einstein postulates, therefore, that no material body can ever move with the velocity of light. He also has shown, mathematically, that if a clock be moved at this immense velocity, it will slow down; that if it could finally reach the velocity of light, it would stop. But laboratory proof of these facts—as opposed to mathematical proof —is difficult because they only appear when objects move at higher speeds than we have so far been able to move them. Jet planes, rockets, and missiles won't do.

But how about some infinitesimally small particle? Might not the atom, say, with its fantastic internal solar system, provide a convenient laboratory?

That, indeed, was the laboratory to which Einstein resorted when his mathematical proofs were challenged. And it was in this laboratory that he evolved the famous equation as a result of which, when inventors used it, more than 150,000 persons died in Japan in August, 1945, and, later, new sources of power for submarines and electric generation began what appears to be an entirely new industrial revolution.

Experiments with radiating atoms soon proved the accuracy of Einstein's mathematical estimates. But once he got into that submicroscopically small world, Einstein made new revolutionary discoveries. The first of these concerned "mass." Mass in physics means not size or weight but inertia or resistance to change of motion. He found that, as a moving body approaches the speed of light, its mass increases. This set him to thinking about the connection between mass and velocity or, in other terms, matter and energy, and under his constant impulse to unify and reduce, he began to wonder if they were not two aspects of the same thing—as ice and steam are both aspects, so to speak, of water! Take radioactive substances such as the one Pierre and Marie Curie had discovered. They emitted particles for thousands of years without greatly reducing their mass. Were not those particles energy? What an immense amount of energy a small quantity of the substance must emit! But was there not some way by which matter could be quickly converted into energy, by splitting its atoms, for instance, thus "destroying" the matter but at the same time releasing what Einstein believed was an amount of energy that could only be expressed in astronomical figures? This belief he expressed in the mathematical equation:

$$E = mc^2$$

in which E represents energy, m represents mass, and c represents the velocity of light. It is immediately apparent that even a small mass, when multiplied by the square of the velocity of light, will produce a huge value of energy.

According to our interpreter, Lincoln Barnett:

This extraordinary relationship becomes more vivid when its terms are translated into concrete values: i.e., one kilogram of coal (about two pounds), if converted *entirely* into energy, would yield 25 billion kilowatt hours of electricity or as much as all the power plants in the U.S. could generate by running steadily for two months.[48]

With his equation, Einstein seems to have shattered two of the most revered laws of orthodox physics: the conservation of matter and the conservation of energy. Actually he has compressed them into a single law by declaring that matter and energy are interchangeable.

Having evolved his formula, he left it to the inventors to devise means of releasing this energy. They have done this by the fission or splitting of the atoms of the highly radioactive element uranium by cyclotrons and other devices.

Einstein went on to other exercises in theoretical physics. Among other things, he found that light as well as matter was subject to the law of gravitation, and this was experimentally proved by a group of British scientists. This led him to the corpuscular theory of light, which says that light consists of particles—and to the reconciliation of this with the wave theory. All this makes exciting reading, but it is easier for the reader who has a mathematical background and cannot concern us here.

Summing up his work in terms of the impulse behind it, Einstein has written:

All of these endeavors are based on the belief that existence should have a completely harmonious structure. Today we have less ground than ever before for allowing ourselves to be forced away from this wonderful belief.[49]

. . .

$$E = mc^2$$

Like waves of light, Einstein's fame spread out over the world after the publication of his first paper, *The Special Theory of Relativity,* in 1905. Four years later, he was appointed Professor Extraordinary of Theoretical Physics in Zurich University. He had remained, since his first year in Switzerland, a Swiss citizen. However, in 1913 his importance had become so great that a special post was created for him—director of the Kaiser-Wilhelm Physical Institute in Berlin—and he had been elected a member of the Royal Prussian Academy of Sciences and given a grant that would permit him to devote all his time to research. He then took back his German citizenship. He could not foretell that the sequence of events which would begin the following year would lead inevitably toward the great tragedy of his life.

In 1915, his *General Theory of Relativity* containing new views on gravitation in the universe was published, and in 1921 he was awarded the Nobel Prize for his discovery of the photoelectric effect—the action of light on electrons. It was early in the 1920's that he made his first visit to America.

For a decade after that he felt the increasing insecurity of Germany and the awful potential of impending change. In those years the honors he received from all over the world, the dozen honorary degrees from universities in Europe and America could not halt the march of doom. From 1930, he was accustomed to spend his winters in Pasadena, California, and his summers in a beautiful villa he had bought in Caputh near Potsdam. When he left for California in the autumn of 1932, he said to his wife:

"Before you leave our villa this time, take a good look at it."

"But why?" she asked.

"Because you will never see it again," Einstein answered. She laughed at him then, but his prediction came true. Adolf Hitler came into power the following year, and Einstein's property and his bank account were confiscated because he was a Jew.

This Nazi ingratitude—rejecting a man who was considered the greatest scientist that ever lived—was America's good fortune. Living out his years as a citizen of the United States, at the Institute for Advanced Studies in Princeton, he was available for consultation in the first developments of the atomic age.

Yet sadness clouded his life after he had left Germany forever. This is poignantly reflected in the book of essays, *Out of My Later Years.* He draws a sharp contrast between the harmony he has found in the universe and the discord in human society. In one of these essays, after telling of the effect on his mind of the evil that came with World War II, he wrote:

> I am firmly convinced that the passionate will for justice and truth has done more to improve man's condition than calculating political shrewdness which in the long run only breeds general disgust. Who can doubt that Moses was a better leader of humanity than Machiavelli? [50]

$$E = mc^2$$

It has been said of Einstein that he was most loved by those who least understood his theories but who were drawn to him by some inscrutable attachment, as if, from his long dwelling amid the music of the spheres, he conveyed the sense of serene harmony that, in the confusion of life, they craved. His barber, the scrubwomen in his house, the gardener at his villa felt for him a sort of worship, and he turned to such people, away from the mathematicians and scientists who crowded around him. It was in the presence of these simple minds that he felt comfort. In such folk the complicated qualities of pretense, of hypocrisy, of duplicity, which brought so much evil into society, were absent. They thought straight and saw life in the simple terms into which, with his colossal intellect, he longed to translate the universe.

To anyone who is standing, still undecided, on the threshold of a career in science—a career that almost irresistibly tempts him, though he may fear its routine—Einstein has given a definition that may carry him over. "The most beautiful thing we can experience," he says, "is the mysterious. It is the source of all true art and science." Today the future is as mysterious as any future mankind has ever faced, and if science and good will can manage to go hand in hand, it may be more beautiful as well.

Bibliography

Section I
BACKGROUND MATERIAL

Ames, Joseph S. "Certain Aspects of Henry's Experiments on Electromagnetic Induction." *Science,* Vol. 75, No. 1934 (January 22, 1932), pp. 87-92.

Arago, D.F.J. *Historical Eloge of James Watt.* Translated from the French by James Patrick Muirhead. London: J. Murray, 1839.

Benz, Francis E. *Pasteur, Knight of the Laboratory.* New York: Dodd, Mead and Company, 1938.

Born, Max. "Physics" (Age of Science Series). *Scientific American,* Vol. 183, No. 3 (September, 1950), pp. 28-31.

Burlingame, Roger. *Inventors Behind the Inventor.* New York: Harcourt, Brace and Company, 1947.

————. *Machines That Built America.* New York: Harcourt, Brace and Company, 1953.

Bush, Vannevar. *Endless Horizons.* Washington, D.C.: Public Affairs Press, 1946.

————. *Science, the Endless Frontier.* Washington, D.C.: U.S. Government Printing Office, 1945.

Calder, Ritchie. *Science in Our Lives.* New York: New American Library of World Literature, 1955.

Curie, Marie. "The Discovery of Radium." An address at Vassar College, May 14, 1921. Published by Vassar College (Ellen S. Richards Monographs, No. 2).

————. *Pierre Curie.* Translated by Charlotte and Vernon Kellogg. New York: The Macmillan Company, 1923.

Dickerson, Edward N. *Joseph Henry and the Magnetic Telegraph.* New York: Charles Scribner's Sons, 1885.

Dickinson, H.W., and Jenkins, Rhys. *James Watt and the Steam Engine.* (Memorial volume for the Watt Centenary Commemoration at Birmingham, 1919.) Oxford: Clarendon Press, 1927.

Dickinson, H.W. and Vowles, H.P. *James Watt and the Industrial Revolution.* London: Published for the British Council by Longmans, Green and Company, 1943.

Dubos, René J. *Louis Pasteur, Free Lance of Science.* Boston: Little, Brown and Company, 1950.

Dunlap, Orrin E., Jr. *Radio's 100 Men of Science.* New York and London: Harper and Brothers, 1944.

Einstein, Albert, and Infeld, Leopold. *The Evolution of Physics.* New York: Simon and Schuster, 1938.

Farey, John. *A Treatise on the Steam Engine.* London: Longmans, Rees, Orme, 1827.

Feinberg, J.G. *The Atom Story.* New York: The Philosophical Library, 1953.

Frank, Philipp. *Einstein, His Life and Times.* Translated from a German manuscript by George Rosen, edited and revised by Shuichi Kusaka. New York: Alfred A. Knopf, 1947.

Freeman, Andrew A., ed. *Brainpower Quest.* New York: The Macmillan Company, 1957.

Fulton, John F., and Thomson, Elizabeth H. *Benjamin Silliman, 1779-1864, Pathfinder in American Science.* New York: H. Schuman, 1947.

Garbedian, H. Gordon. *Albert Einstein, Maker of Universes.* New York and London: Funk and Wagnalls Company, 1939.

Gumpert, Martin. *Trail Blazers of Science.* New York: Funk and Wagnalls Company, 1936.

Harrow, Benjamin. *From Newton to Einstein.* New York: D. Van Nostrand Company, 1920.

Hart, Ivor B. *James Watt and the History of Steam Power.* New York: H. Schuman, 1949.

Henry, Joseph. "Contributions to Electricity and Magnetism." *Transactions,* American Philosophical Society, Vol. 6. Reprinted in pamphlet form, Philadelphia: James Kay, Jun., and Brother, 1839.

———. "On the Production of Currents and Sparks of Electricity from Magnetism." *American Journal of Science,* Vol. 22 (July, 1832), pp. 403 ff.

———. *The Scientific Writings of Joseph Henry.* 2 vols. Washington, D.C.: Smithsonian Institution, 1886.

Henry, Mary A. "The Invention of the Electromagnetic Telegraph." *Electrical World,* Vol. 26 (Nov. 23-Dec. 21, 1895).

Hogben, Lancelot. *Mathematics for the Million.* New York: W.W. Norton and Company, 1937.

———. *Science for the Citizen.* New York: Alfred A. Knopf, 1938.

Jaffe, Bernard. *Men of Science in America.* New York: Simon and Schuster, 1944.

Jeans, Sir James. *The Growth of Physical Science.* New York: The Macmillan Company, 1948.

Kovarik, Alois F. "Pupin, Michael Idvorsky." *Dictionary of American Biography.* New York: Charles Scribner's Sons, 1944, Supplement One, pp. 611-615.

Leonard, Jonathan N. *Crusaders in Chemistry:* Six Makers of the Modern World. Garden City, N.Y.: Doubleday, Doran and Company, 1930.

————. *Enjoyment of Science.* Garden City, N.Y.: Doubleday, Doran and Company, 1942.

Magie, William F. "Henry, Joseph." *Dictionary of American Biography.* New York: Charles Scribner's Sons, 1932, Vol. VIII, pp. 550-553.

Marshall, T.H. *James Watt.* Boston: Small, Maynard and Company, 1925.

Mellanby, Alexander L. "James Watt." (An oration delivered in the University of Glasgow on Commemoration Day, June 17, 1936.) Glasgow: Printed by the University, 1936.

Muirhead, James Patrick. *The Life of James Watt.* London: J. Murray, 1858.

Oppenheimer, J. Robert. *Science and the Common Understanding.* New York: Simon and Schuster, 1954.

Otto, Max. *Science and the Moral Life.* New York: New American Library of World Literature, 1949.

Pupin, Michael I. "Our Debt to Joseph Henry." *The American Scholar,* Vol. 2, No. 2 (March, 1933).

Russell, Bertrand. *The Impact of Science on Society.* New York: Simon and Schuster, 1953.

Sarton, George. *The Life of Science* (Essays in the History of Civilization). New York: H. Schuman, 1948.

Silliman, Benjamin. *Journal of Travels in England, Holland and Scotland . . . in the Years 1805-1806.* 3rd ed. rev. and enl. in 3 vols. New Haven: S. Converse, 1820.

Slosson, Edwin E. *Easy Lessons in Einstein.* New York: Harcourt, Brace and Company, 1921.

Smiles, Samuel. *Lives of Boulton and Watt.* New York: Charles Scribner's Sons, 1904.

United States, National Science Foundation. *Annual Reports.* Washington, D.C., 1950-1958.

United States, National Science Foundation. *Basic Research as a National Resource.* Washington, 1957.

Van Nostrand's Scientific Encyclopedia. 3rd ed. New York: D. Van Nostrand and Company, 1958.

Warren, Charles H. "Silliman, Benjamin." *Dictionary of American Biography.* New York: Charles Scribner's Sons, 1935, Vol. XVII, pp. 160-163.

Wilson, Mitchell A. *American Science and Invention.* New York: Simon and Schuster, 1954.

Wood, Laura N. *Louis Pasteur.* New York: Julian Messner, 1948.

Bibliography

Section II
SOURCE MATERIAL FOR QUOTATIONS

1. Fortune, Editors of. *The Mighty Force of Research*. New York: McGraw-Hill Book Company, 1956, p. 27.
2. Fortune, Editors of. *The Mighty Force of Research,* p. 39.
3. Ramsay, Sir William. *The Life and Letters of Joseph Black, M.D.* London: Constable and Company, Ltd., 1918, p. 9.
4. Brougham, Lord Henry. *Lives of Men of Letters and Science Who Flourished in the Time of George III.* London: Charles Knight and Company, 1845, p. 347.
5. Black, Joseph. *Lectures on the Elements of Chemistry* delivered in the University of Edinburgh and published from his manuscripts by John Robison. 3 vols. Philadelphia, 1806-1807. Vol. I, p. 168.
6. Dickinson, H.W. *James Watt, Craftsman and Engineer.* Cambridge: Cambridge University Press, 1936, p. 36.
7. Clerke, Agnes Mary. "Black, Joseph." *Dictionary of National Biography.* London: Oxford University Press, 1921, Vol. 2, p. 573.
8. Fisher, George P. *Life of Benjamin Silliman.* 2 vols. New York: Charles Scribner and Company, 1866. Vol. 1, pp. 6-7.
9. Fisher, George P. *Life of Benjamin Silliman.* Vol. I, p. 88.

10. Fisher, George P. *Life of Benjamin Silliman.* Vol. I, p. 88.
11. Fisher, George P. *Life of Benjamin Silliman.* Vol. I, p. 102.
12. Fisher, George P. *Life of Benjamin Silliman.* Vol. I, p. 104.
13. Silliman, Benjamin, ed. *The American Journal of Science and Arts.* New Haven, Vol. I (1818), No. 1, Prefatory Announcement.
14. Silliman, Benjamin, ed. *The American Journal of Science and Arts.* Vol. L (1847), No. 1, Preface.
15. Smithsonian Institution. *A Memorial of Joseph Henry,* published by order of Congress. Washington: Government Printing Office, 1880, pp. 55-56.
16. Coulson, Thomas. *Joseph Henry, His Life and Work.* Princeton, N.J.: Princeton University Press, 1950, p. 15.
17. Silliman, Benjamin, ed. *The American Journal of Science and Arts.* Vol. XIX, Jan. 1831, p. 404.
18. Crowther, J. G. *Famous American Men of Science.* New York: W. W. Norton and Company, 1937, letter to Rev. S. B. Dod, p. 182.
19. Silliman, Benjamin, ed. *The American Journal of Science and Arts.* Vol. XX, July, 1831, p. 340.
20. Vallery-Radot, René. *The Life of Pasteur.* Translated from the French by Mrs. R.L. Devonshire. New York: Doubleday, Doran and Company, 1923, p. 416.
21. Vallery-Radot, René. *The Life of Pasteur,* p. 15.
22. Vallery-Radot, René. *The Life of Pasteur,* p. 120.
23. Vallery-Radot, René. *The Life of Pasteur,* p. 141.
24. Vallery-Radot, René. *The Life of Pasteur,* p. 260.
25. Vallery-Radot, René. *The Life of Pasteur,* pp. 260-261.
26. Vallery-Radot, René. *The Life of Pasteur,* p. 444.
27. Vallery-Radot, René. *The Life of Pasteur,* p. 343.

28. Pupin, Michael I. *From Immigrant to Inventor.* New York: Charles Scribner's Sons, 1923, p. 76.
29. Pupin, Michael I. *From Immigrant to Inventor,* p. 78.
30. Pupin, Michael I. *From Immigrant to Inventor,* p. 98.
31. Pupin, Michael I. *From Immigrant to Inventor,* p. 110.
32. Pupin, Michael I. *From Immigrant to Inventor,* p. 307.
33. Pupin, Michael I. *From Immigrant to Inventor,* p. 307.
34. Pupin, Michael I. *From Immigrant to Inventor,* p. 356.
35. Pupin, Michael I. *From Immigrant to Inventor,* pp. 335-336.
36. Curie, Eve. *Madame Curie.* Translated by Vincent Sheean. Garden City, N.Y.: Doubleday, Doran and Company, 1937, p. 39.
37. Curie, Eve. *Madame Curie,* p. 42.
38. Curie, Eve. *Madame Curie,* p. 94.
39. Ferris, Helen, ed. *When I Was a Girl:* The Stories of Five Famous Women as Told by Themselves. New York: The Macmillan Company, 1930, p. 153.
40. Curie, Eve. *Madame Curie,* p. 164.
41. Curie, Eve. *Madame Curie,* p. 170.
42. Curie, Eve. *Madame Curie,* pp. 170-171.
43. Curie, Eve. *Madame Curie,* p. 175.
44. Barnett, Lincoln. *The Universe and Dr. Einstein.* Mentor Edition. New York: New American Library of World Literature, 1952, pp. 44-45.
45. Barnett, Lincoln. *The Universe and Dr. Einstein,* p. 48.
46. Barnett, Lincoln. *The Universe and Dr. Einstein,* p. 49.
47. Barnett, Lincoln. *The Universe and Dr. Einstein,* p. 51.
48. Barnett, Lincoln. *The Universe and Dr. Einstein,* p. 70.
49. Einstein, Albert. *Essays in Science.* New York: The Philosophical Library, 1954, p. 114.
50. Einstein, Albert. *Out of My Later Years.* New York: The Philosophical Library, 1950, p. 10.

Index

185